A REMEDY FOR MEDICAL COMPLAINTS

A PRACTITIONER'S GUIDE TO COMPLAINTS PROCEDURES

by

Rosamund Rhodes-Kemp
Solicitor, Russell Jones & Walker

London
Sweet & Maxwell
1998

Published in 1998 by Sweet & Maxwell Limited
100 Avenue Road
London NW3 3PF
(http://www.smlawpub.co.uk)

Typeset by Dataword Services Ltd of Chilcompton
Printed and bound in Great Britain by
MPG Books Ltd, Bodmin, Cornwall

No natural forests were destroyed to make this product;
only farmed timber was used and replanted.

ISBN 0 421 60000 4

A CIP catalogue record for this book is available
from the British Library

For my father, the late Professor Duncan Williams,
and my husband Ray, with gratitude and love for all their
help and encouragement both past and present.

ACKNOWLEDGMENTS

May I offer my gratitude and appreciation to all the organisations and people listed below who have kindly allowed me to reproduce information from their existing literature, answered additional questions, provided their own material or checked particular sections for accuracy. Without their help this book would not have been possible:

Ruth Powell (*Solicitor, Russell Jones & Walker*)
The British Acupuncture Council
The British Chiropractic Association
The Chartered Society of Physiotherapy
The Royal College of Speech and Language Therapists
The Council for Professions Supplementary To Medicine
The General Council and Register of Osteopaths
The General Dental Council
The General Medical Council
The General Optical Council
The Royal Pharmaceutical Society of Great Britain
The Society of Homeopathy
The Society of Osteopaths
The UKCC
The Wilson Committee

A special mention should also be made of the sterling work by my secretary, Stephanie Banczyk-Sturgeon, who not only typed the manuscript but also thought of the title. Secondly, Kim Richards, who picked up the tab at the end by dealing with amendments. Finally, Gillian Solly, who encouraged me throughout, particularly in the early stages when heavy commitments meant it was tempting to quit. Any inaccuracies in the text are entirely my own responsibility.

TABLE OF CONTENTS

ix

TABLES OF CONTENTS

APPENDICES

CHAPTER 1

INTRODUCTION

Over the last 20 years, litigation in respect of medical treatment **1–01** has increased dramatically. The Comptroller and Auditor General disclosed in his annual report on the National Health Service (NHS) that health authorities and Trusts paid out about £200 million in 1995/1996 to meet the cost of clinical negligence.[1]

The steep rise has been attributed to many factors including: **1–02**

— the decline in deference to professionals generally;

— a demand for more accountability for those working within the public sector;

— an increasing awareness of a patient's rights, for example through the Patients' Charter;

— greater expectations regarding medical treatment and achievable outcomes; and

— media interest and coverage of health issues.

These are in part societal changes and not just related to **1–03** health care. Nonetheless, the fanfare regarding the restructuring of the NHS and the consumer market type language of purchaser and provider, and even of proposed league tables for hospitals and individual Consultants, has heightened the public demand for accountability. It has arguably also raised expectations to unrealistic levels, bearing in mind the financial restraints on the NHS which has to rely primarily upon public funds raised through taxation.

---

[1] *Daily Telegraph*, July 1997.

1–04   In some ways perhaps, the changes can be said to have been positive—the old paternalism which resulted in health care professionals withholding important information about diagnoses and prognosis for some patients in their "best interest", and the lack of information before surgery, is being replaced by more openness and better communication between carer and patient. That must be for the good. Also, while the old paternalistic attitude may have been founded in good intention, in application it could often lead to a failure to respect a patient's rights, and most importantly in this context, the inviolability of the patient's body. This was referred to in an important medical law case as *"the right to physical integrity and the human dignity it protects"*.[2]

1–05   Along with the decline in deference and the demand for greater accountability and a reasonable standard of care, litigation has also increased. Some commentators feel that the pendulum has swung too far in the direction of legal proceedings and that the costs, both financial and emotional, are too high. Moves have been made to redress the balance, for example the Legal Aid Board has suggested that applicants should have exhausted the Health Service complaints procedures before an application for legal aid for a medical negligence claim will be considered. More recent changes regarding provision of legal aid will affect availability of legal aid for those seeking to investigate claims for injury as a consequence of poor medical treatment. Lord Woolf, who carried out a review of the whole of the civil litigation process, has put forward quite distinct proposals regarding medical negligence claims including consideration of alternative means of resolving medical disputes.

1–06   The complexity of the law on this topic is itself sufficient to deter most potential litigants. It can never be said that it is easy for a patient to succeed in discharging the necessary burden of proof in order to be successful in a medical negligence claim. The two-pronged test is onerous. He/she has to prove that the standard of care provided fell below that which would be considered acceptable by a responsible body of medical men in the field. If even a minority consider the care reasonable or,

---

[2] Brennan J. in *Department of Health and Community Services v. J.W.B. and S.M.B.* (1992) 66 A.L.R. 300.

within acceptable boundaries, then the claim will fail. Bearing in mind the divergence in medical opinion and the fact that a huge variety of treatments could all fall within acceptable boundaries, it is easy to see how proving substandard care can actually be extremely difficult.

If the patient manages to establish that the doctor has been **1–07** negligent, he/she must go on to prove what damage has been caused as a consequence of the medical treatment as opposed to any underlying condition. Again, this is not necessarily straightforward when you consider that the reason a patient goes for medical treatment in the first place is because of an accident or a medical condition. It is therefore necessary to measure the difference between the expected outcome of treatment and the actual outcome of substandard treatment. This process can in itself be fraught with difficulty.

Apart from anything else, funding these claims is problematic. **1–08** They are expensive, largely because of the reliance on expert medical evidence from busy clinicians who have to set time aside in order to prepare reports and to attend meetings and even court. Very few individuals in our society can afford to fund these claims privately. The restrictions on legal aid look set to continue and may indeed increase so that the number of individuals eligible for legal aid will inevitably become smaller and smaller.

Alternative means of funding, such as conditional fee agree- **1–09** ments, are not yet readily available for these claims because of the high risk nature of the litigation. It is very difficult to say at the outset, *i.e.* before obtaining the medical records and expert medical opinion, whether the claim is going to succeed or not, and so finding insurance at an early stage is often impossible.

Apart from the difficulties encountered in progressing medi- **1–10** cal negligence claims it is often said that most patients do not want monetary compensation. Rather they would like an explanation of what happened, an admission of responsibility, an apology and reassurance that the same accident will not occur again. Legal proceedings can provide some, if not all of these, but often only after years of battling and only as a by-product of the claim which is essentially for monetary compensation. For many litigants financial awards are necessary: for example, a widow with two children whose husband has been killed as a result of a doctor's negligence, or a brain-damaged child whose

3

parents desperately need funds to provide proper nursing care and equipment. However, money is not always necessary or wanted by all those making a complaint or going to see a lawyer for advice after a medical accident.

1–11   The best advice to give anyone seeking medical treatment is to check the credentials and qualifications of the person providing the treatment. It is always better to prevent accidents then put matters right afterwards. However, even with the best will in the world on all sides, complaints about treatment and medical accidents will arise.

1–12   So where does this leave the patient who is dissatisfied or harmed as a consequence of medical treatment, who either does not want to initiate a legal claim or cannot afford to do so, or who could not satisfy the "burden of proof"?

1–13   The answer is hopefully contained within this book which provides a guide to what to do when things go wrong with medical treatment inside and outside the NHS. An explanation is provided of what procedures are involved in making a complaint about medical treatment to various professional organisations and what the patient can expect to achieve by processing a formal complaint.

1–14   These procedures are not about compensation, or gaining a moral victory; they are a way of formalising a legitimate complaint and holding the health care provider accountable, alerting the professional organisation to a potential problem and improving the standard of care through a process of reporting and recording substandard treatment.

1–15   The purpose of this book is to provide a user-friendly guide to making formal complaints about medical treatment. Although the NHS complaints procedure is covered in the text, the book is not solely concerned with care given within the framework of the NHS. Rather, the aim is to enable practitioners to advise clients, *i.e.* former patients receiving treatment from all sources, including alternative therapies, to register dissatisfaction with the treatment received if it is felt to have been of a poor standard, dangerous or ill-considered.

1–16   Unfortunately, it became clear during the writing of this book that unlike the NHS complaints procedures which are well publicised and accessible, those for the majority of allied health care organisations range from good to obscure to incomprehensible. Some are, however, much better than others, but in the present era there is certainly a need for far greater accessibility to these procedures. Under these circumstances the need for a comprehensive guide became all the more apparent.

The information is set out in a way which will enable **1–17** practitioners to advise clients, or provide patients themselves with the necessary steps to complain formally about treatment from GPs to acupuncturists, physiotherapists to chiropodists. These procedures are separate from, but not necessarily a substitute for, legal proceedings.

The book can also be used by those advising in Citizens **1–18** Advice Bureaux, law centres or community health councils regarding patients' rights when problems arise in relation to medical treatment.

It may seem strange that a lawyer specialising in medical **1–19** negligence litigation should write a book designed to provide advice on alternatives to the litigation process. However, as a former nurse and now a lawyer, I have always tried to do what is best for patients. At the same time, I remain committed to the National Health Service and to the growing use of alternative medicine which can so usefully complement traditional medical care. The service provided by these health professionals is one of which we can all justly be proud. I very much hope that this book will help patients and Health Service providers by encouraging those dissatisfied with medical treatment to look first to the professionals themselves for an explanation of what went wrong and, if appropriate, an apology and sanction against the person responsible. By the same process the profession can learn lessons and improve standards in the future.

Rosamund Rhodes-Kemp
January 1998

CHAPTER TWO

HOSPITAL DOCTORS AND GENERAL PRACTITIONERS

SECTION 1: NHS COMPLAINTS

INTRODUCTION

On April 1, 1996 a new NHS complaints procedure was **2–01** introduced. This replaced the previous hospital and GP complaints procedures with a single two stage procedure.

The change was in response to a growing number of concerns **2–02** about the previous "hotch-potch" system, including those of lack of openness, inaccessibility, perceived unfairness of the system and the time it took for an investigation to be completed. Also, the system for complaints to Trusts and GPs differed widely, with GP complaints being inappropriately tied to GP contractual obligations under their terms and conditions of service.

The aim of the new system is to make complaining simpler, **2–03** quicker and more accessible and to encourage greater openness, thus increasing patient satisfaction and maintaining consumer confidence.

The new system has the following main stages: **2–04**

1. **Local resolution**

2. **Independent review**

If a complainant is still not satisfied with the outcome of a **2–05** complaint, it is possible for the matter to be referred to the Health Service Ombudsman, whose jurisdiction has been extended to cover GP care and clinical care in the hospital setting. These stages apply whether the complaint is about a hospital doctor or nurse, a GP, an NHS pharmacist or a member of the ambulance service.

7

3. Health Service Ombudsman

2–06 An investigation by the Ombudsman's office is sometimes known as the Third Stage.

2–07 It is important to stress that these procedures are designed solely to deal with complaints and are not connected with disciplinary issues which are quite separate. This may seem strange but it is actually designed to encourage staff co-operation and willingness to participate in the new system, otherwise its efficiency would be diminished. It is also true to say that if a complaint concerns conduct sufficiently serious to warrant disciplinary action, steps would be taken to instigate the disciplinary procedure; but patients should not be under the impression that there is an automatic link.

A. PERSONNEL INVOLVED IN THE NEW COMPLAINTS PROCEDURE

2–08 The Government's implementation guidelines for the local resolution stage are very general, leaving it up to the hospital or GP practice to design their own procedures. However, most of the procedures introduced are very similar for all Trusts and GP surgeries.

2–09 When the changes were introduced, a lot of emphasis was placed on the training of Health Service staff to deal with complaints in a positive and proactive way. Unfortunately, it seems that resources, *i.e.* cash, and indeed time for this training were not forthcoming. Final guidelines on the procedure were only sent to Trusts and GPs at the last minute and there was something of a scramble to introduce the measures on time. As a consequence, it has taken a while for staff to become familiar with what exactly is expected of them. There are a number of new names for personnel dealing with complaints so it might be helpful to set out who is actually involved and what they are called.

2–10 It is important to appreciate, however, that when making a formal written complaint, these should be addressed to the *NHS Trust complaints manager* if the care was given in hospital or the *local health authority complaints manager* if the care was given by a GP, a dentist, or in the community.

1. All staff

Basically, all Health Service personnel are expected to be ready, **2–11** willing and able to respond to complaints by patients or their relatives. Some Trusts have initiated training procedures to ensure that staff are taught how to deal with complaints.

2. Complaints Managers

In addition, complaints managers have been appointed to each **2–12** NHS Trust and Health Authority. Complaints managers at the NHS Trust deal with NHS hospitals, community and ambulance services; the complaints manager at the health authority deals with complaints involving GPs, NHS dentists, pharmacists and opticians. Resources were not available to create posts as such and so often existing personnel were asked to become complaints managers or told that would be an additional part of their job. Therefore some complaints managers are perhaps a lot more skilful and senior than others. The service they provide may vary accordingly.

In relation to GP practices, someone has been appointed in **2–13** each practice to be responsible for the initial handling of complaints and a leaflet is available in every GP surgery explaining who that person is and how complaints are investigated. This may or may not be a complaints manager.

3. Conciliators

Most health authorities have also appointed a conciliator to help **2–14** mediate between the complainant and the staff concerned. Conciliators are independent of GP practices and Trusts and are experienced in helping to mediate in complaints. GP surgeries are more likely to involve a conciliator than an NHS Trust.

4. Convenor

Each NHS Trust/health authority has also appointed a com- **2–15** plaints convenor who only becomes involved in a complaint if the complainant is not satisfied with the results of the local resolution stage and seeks to take the matter further, *i.e.* to the second stage: an independent review. The convenor is the person responsible for deciding whether or not a review should take place and convening a panel to carry out the review. He or she is a non-executive director of the health authority or Trust.

9

5. Health Services Ombudsman

2–16 The Ombudsman is a senior civil servant who has always had jurisdiction to investigate complaints about maladministration within the Health Service. However, under the new system, his jurisdiction has now been extended considerably to cover complaints about the standard of clinical care in the hospital environment and the standard of GP care. Previously, he was not allowed to consider complaints about either of these areas. He has increased the number of staff in his effort to cope with the probable increase in work and he has also appointed medical and nursing advisors to comment on the standard of care provided.

2–17 However, the Ombudsman remains the last resort and matters can only be referred to the Ombudsman once the local resolution and independent review stages are exhausted and if the complainant remains dissatisfied.

B. TIME LIMITS

2–18 Complaints should be made within *six months* of the date of the incident, or *six months* of discovering the problem provided that this is within *12 months* of the incident.

2–19 It is worth noting that the Health Information Service can provide up to date information regarding the NHS complaints system. The telephone number is 0800 665544.

FIRST STAGE—LOCAL RESOLUTION

2–20 This can be divided into minor and more serious complaints.

Minor complaints

2–21 These can be dealt with straight away, either orally or in writing, and can be made to ward or hospital staff, a patient's GP or someone else in the GP practice.

2–22 If a patient or relative feels awkward about complaining to the actual GP practice, he or she can make a complaint to the complaints manager at the health authority. The aim is that most of these minor complaints can be dealt with on the spot by frontline staff as an everyday part of patient care without having to call upon more formal procedures. All members of the health care team, whether they are doctors, nurses, dentists, midwives, receptionists, physiotherapists, should be ready, willing and able to respond to complaints from patients or their relatives.

If the person to whom a complaint is made is unable to deal **2–23** with the complaint then they must ensure that it is passed to an appropriate person who can respond to the complaint more fully.

If the complaint cannot be dealt with immediately, then the **2–24** complaints manager—in a GP surgery this might be one of the doctors; in a dental practice, one of the dentists or practice managers—should advise what will happen next, how the complaint is going to be dealt with and particularly, if the complaint is about a failure in care, whether a meeting is going to be arranged to discuss the matter and if so, how it will be arranged.

A minor complaint can be made orally or in writing and the **2–25** response will be orally or in writing, depending upon the seriousness of the complaint. A complainant may wish to seek the advice of his or her local community health council (CHC) at this stage but that will be unlikely if the complaint is fairly minor.

More serious complaints

All GP surgeries and hospitals should have leaflets and informa- **2–26** tion concerning how complaints can be made. The first thing a complainant should do is ask for this information.

The form the investigation will take and the level of the **2–27** complainant's involvement in the process will vary depending on the nature and seriousness of the complaint. However, if the complaint is not one that can be dealt with immediately, then the complainant should have an acknowledgment of the complaint within *two days* or a response within *five days* in relation to GP care and whenever possible, either a written response or a meeting to resolve the complaint within *10 working days* of the complaint being made. If it is going to take longer than 10 working days to investigate the complaint, then the complainant should be informed.

The health authority may arrange for a meeting with the GP/ **2–28** dentist/pharmacist concerned and may possibly arrange for a conciliator to attend if it is felt that that would be appropriate and helpful to resolve the issue. Otherwise, a written response will be within *10 working days* of the complaint and this will include:

(i) an explanation of what happened;

(ii) notification that a meeting is going to be called; and

(iii) if applicable, advice that the investigation may take longer than 10 days and why.

2–29   In relation to a complaint involving a Trust or the ambulance service, then an investigation may include the following stages:

(i) a meeting with the individuals involved, the complaints manager and possibly the complainant;

(ii) a formal inquiry;

(iii) interviews with the staff involved;

(iv) obtaining the opinion of senior doctors on the standard of care provided.

2–30   Regarding NHS Trusts it is a requirement that the investigation be completed within *20 working days* of receipt of the complaint.

2–31   At the conclusion of the local resolution stage, where the complaint involves an NHS Trust or Family Health Services, a complainant should receive a written report including:

(i) an explanation of what happened;

(ii) an apology, if appropriate;

(iii) indication of what preventative steps will be taken to ensure that the same thing does not happen again; and

(iv) notice of the right to seek an independent review if the complainant is still not satisfied.

SECOND STAGE—INDEPENDENT REVIEW

2–32 If a complainant is not happy with the results of the local resolution stage, she/he should write to the health authority convenor/NHS Trust convenor. In either case, the request must reach the convenor within *20 working days* of the complainant receiving the results of the local resolution. The complainant must ask for an independent review. The convenor must acknowledge the request within *two days*. The convenor will ask the complainant to provide a statement setting out:

(i) remaining grievances, *i.e.* those not dealt with by the local resolution stage; and

(ii) why the complainant is dissatisfied with the outcome of the local resolution.

N.B. There is no automatic right to an independent review so it is important that the complainant provides sufficient justification in the statement. A complainant would usually be best advised to seek help from his or her local community health council (CHC) in the preparation of this statement.

The convenor for an NHS Trust aims to make a decision **2–33** about an independent review within *20 working days* and a convenor for a health authority will make a decision within *10 working days.*

There are two options open to the convenor: first, to refuse **2–34** the request and secondly to agree.

Refusal of a Request for an Independent Review
A refusal must include: **2–35**

(i) an explanation as to why the request has been refused; this may be because in the convenor's view, all the grounds have been covered during the local resolution stage and an independent review would not take the matter further or provide a different answer;

(ii) advice about the complainant's right to approach the health service Ombudsman.

Agreement to an Independent Review
An agreement should include details of which aspects of the **2–36** complaint the panel will be investigating—this is because some aspects will have been adequately covered at the local resolution stage.

It should be noted that to convene an independent review panel is a costly and time-consuming business and therefore it is likely that a significant proportion of requests will be refused; although the decision can be appealed by writing to the health service Ombudsman, there is certainly an element of discretion built into the convenor's role and it is likely that a reversal of the decision to refuse will be a relatively rare occurrence.

Having made a decision to proceed, a convenor has to **2–37** appoint a review panel within 20 working days of informing the complainant of a decision to convene a panel (NHS Trust) or 10 working days if the complaint involved family health services, *i.e.* GPs, dentists, pharmacists, etc.

Independent Review

2–38 If the convenor agrees that there should be an independent review of the complaint, the complainant should be notified of the fact that a panel will be set up, then the panel will look at the complaint, talk to everyone involved and get specialist advice as appropriate. The convenor will inform the complainant of the matters that are to be investigated by the panel (the terms of reference).

2–39 In making these inquiries and setting up the panel, the convenor will be advised by an independent lay person who is appointed by the regional office of the NHS executive; he/she cannot just make the decision on his/her own. The panel will consist of the following:

(i) an independent lay chairperson;

(ii) the convenor;

(iii) an independent lay person—for Trust complaints this will be someone from the health authority or the GP fundholder who paid for the service about which the complaint is made. In family health service complaints it will be a person from a list held by the regional office of the NHS executive;

(iv) at least two independent clinical assessors (for clinical complaints only).

2–40 The panel chair is appointed by the regional office of the NHS executive and decides how to conduct the review. Some will bring all the people involved together in a meeting to discuss the complaint. Others may decide to see the complainant and the person complained about separately. If the complainant has a view about this he/she can tell the convenor. The panel will meet in private and will be confidential. The Community Health Council can advise the complainant both before the meeting and indeed the complainant is allowed to have someone from the community health council present at the meeting.

14

Also, a complainant who is called to an interview or meeting is entitled to be accompanied by a person of his/her own choosing who can, with the agreement of the chair person, speak on the complainant's behalf. However, the person who accompanies the complainant cannot act as an advocate if they are legally qualified. The complainant may also be accompanied by a second person, such as a relative for emotional support.

The panel will have access to relevant documents, including, **2–41** where appropriate, the complainant's health records. The complainant does not have the right to see the papers that go to the panel but he or she can ask to do so.

The panel will then prepare a report setting out the results of **2–42** the investigation, together with conclusions and any comments and suggestions. This report will be in draft form and the complainant will be sent a copy. If the complaint is about an NHS Trust then the first draft report should be made available within *50 working days* of the panel being formally established; but if the complaint involves a family health services matter, then the time allowed for the first draft report is *30 working days* of the panel being formally established.

The complainant is entitled to comment on the first draft **2–43** report and a final report should be sent to the complainant within *15 working days* of the draft report.

The aim is that the review should be completed within *six* **2–44** *months* of the complainant's request for independent review (the Trust and health authority complaints) or *three months* for family health services complaints.

The final report will also be sent to the chief executive of the **2–45** Trust or health authority and he/she in turn should write to the complainant to inform them what action, if any, will be taken as the result of the independent review and to advise the complainant of his/her right to complaint to the Ombudsman if still dissatisfied with the outcome.

THIRD STAGE—THE HEALTH SERVICE OMBUDSMAN

If the complainant is not happy with the way his or her **2–46** complaint has been dealt with, either because of the refusal of an independent review or dissatisfaction with the outcome of the Review, it is open to the complainant to ask the Health Service Ombudsman to investigate the complaint.

2–47   The Ombudsman is totally independent of the NHS and can investigate complaints that are about:

(i) poor service;

(ii) failure to purchase or provide a service that a patient is entitled to receive;

(iii) administrative failures—avoidable delays, not following the proper procedures, rudeness or discourtesy, not explaining decisions, not answering a complaint within the time limits set down in the new procedure, etc.;

(iv) care and treatment provided by a doctor, nurse or other trained professional—if the event happened *after March 31, 1996*;

(v) GPs, dentists, pharmacists or opticians providing NHS services—if the event happened *after March 31, 1996*; or

(vi) failure to provide information under the Code of Practice on openness in the NHS.

2–48   A complainant should write to the Ombudsman giving details of his or her complaint. A leaflet produced by the Ombudsman's office is available from the Ombudsman, Citizens Advice Bureaux and community health councils and this provides more detailed information and, importantly, a form that the complainant can use.

2–49   A complaint to the Ombudsman should be in writing and should include:

(a) a description of what happened, when and where and—if possible—who was involved;

(b) an explanation as to why the complainant is complaining and *that the complainant has already been through the local complaints procedure*; and

(c) all the available evidence, *e.g.* copy letters and any background papers. If originals are sent, photocopies will be taken and the originals returned promptly but obviously it is much easier for the Ombudsman office staff if copies are sent in the first instance.

Time Limit

A complainant must make a complaint to the Ombudsman 2–50 within *12 months* of realising that there is a complaint. The Ombudsman can extend the period in extenuating circumstances, for example, if the local procedure has taken overlong, but a complainant cannot rely on this discretion being exercised.

Moreover, it is up to the Ombudsman to decide whether to 2–51 investigate the complaint or not. It is highly unlikely that an Ombudsman will investigate any case that has not first been through the NHS complaints procedure.

If the Ombudsman does refuse to investigate further, then the 2–52 complainant will be given reasons.

If the Ombudsman decides to investigate the complaint, then 2–53 the complainant will be sent details of the matters which the Ombudsman will investigate.

The Ombudsman's investigation will include an examination 2–54 of the medical records, possibly interviews with those individuals concerned both staff and the complainant and sometimes an on the spot investigation into the case, *i.e.* where the complaint arose.

The complainant is sent a report of the Ombudsman's 2–55 findings. If any part of the complaint is upheld then the report will also say whether the NHS authority has agreed to remedy any injustice or hardship. For example, a complainant may be offered an apology or advised that there has been a change of policy or procedure. *N.B.* There is no appeal against the Ombudsman's decision.

PRIVATE MEDICAL SERVICES

If a client has a complaint about private treatment, he or she 2–56 should write and complain to the hospital or practitioner concerned. The way that the service deals with the complaint will depend on its own procedure. If a complainant is not satisfied then his or her only option is to take legal action.

NHS PATIENTS IN PRIVATE SERVICES

If the complainant is an NHS patient who was sent to a private 2–57 service and was not happy with the standard of care provided, then he or she should write and complain directly to the service provider and send a copy of the complaint to the complaints manager at the health authority or the GP who purchased the care. If a complainant is not satisfied with the reply, he or she should write to the health authority under the NHS complaints procedure.

2–58   If the complainant remains dissatisfied, he or she can ask for an independent review. Where a health authority or GP fund holder has purchased the service concerned, the complainant should make a complaint to the health authority and ask for an independent review. If a Trust has purchased the service, the complainant can ask the complaints manager for an independent review.

2–59   The Health Service Ombudsman can look into complaints against private hospitals or nursing homes where care and treatment was paid for by the NHS.

TABLE 1: GP/NHS DENTIST/FAMILY HEALTH SERVICES COMPLAINTS PROCEDURES

COMPLAINTS TO: Local Health Authority Complaints Manager

TIME LIMITS

Complaints should be made within:

— six months of the incident; or

— six months of discovering the problem provided that this is within 12 months of the incident.

FIRST STAGE—LOCAL RESOLUTION

MINOR COMPLAINT

MORE SERIOUS COMPLAINT

DEALT WITH STRAIGHT AWAY: RESPONSE MAY BE ORAL ONLY

ACKNOWLEDGMENT WITHIN **TWO DAYS** RESPONSE WITHIN **FIVE DAYS**

Community Health Council

COMPLAINANT SHOULD RECEIVE WRITTEN RESPONSE WITHIN **10 WORKING DAYS**

TO INCLUDE:
(1) An explanation of what happened.
(2) Notification that a meeting is going to be called.
(3) Advice, if appropriate that investigation may take 10 days to complete.

At the end of the local resolution stage the complainant should receive:

(1) Explanation of what happened.

(2) Details of anything agreed at meeting.

(3) Steps which will be taken to prevent the problem occurring.

(4) Advice on complainant's right to request an independent review.

SECOND STAGE—INDEPENDENT REVIEW

> IF COMPLAINANT IS NOT HAPPY WITH THE RESULT OF THE LOCAL RESOLUTION STAGE S/HE SHOULD WRITE TO THE HEALTH AUTHORITY CONVENOR — MUST REACH THE CONVENOR WITHIN **20 WORKING DAYS** OF COMPLAINANT RECEIVING RESULTS OF LOCAL RESOLUTION—AND ASK FOR AN INDEPENDENT REVIEW.

> CONVENOR MUST ACKNOWLEDGE REQUEST WITHIN **TWO DAYS**.

Convenor will ask complainant to provide a statement setting out:

(1) Remaining grievances.

(2) Why complainant is dissatisfied with outcome of local resolution.

N.B.: There is no automatic right to an independent review so it is important that the complainant provides sufficient justification in the statement. Local CHC can help prepare the statement.

> CONVENOR AIMS TO MAKE A DECISION ABOUT AN INDEPENDENT REVIEW WITHIN **10 WORKING DAYS**

REFUSAL to include:

(1) Explanation as to why refused.

(2) Complainant's right to approach the Health Service Ombudsman.

AGREEMENT to include:

(1) Details of which aspects of the complaint the panel will be investigating.

PANEL WILL BE APPOINTED WITHIN **10 WORKING DAYS** OF CONVENOR INFORMING COMPLAINANT OF DECISION TO CONVENE A PANEL

PANEL TO CONSIST OF:

(1) An independent lay chairperson.

(2) The convenor.

(3) Independent lay member or representative of the purchaser.

(4) At least two independent clinical assessors (clinical complaints only).

INVESTIGATION BY:

(1) Interviewing by those involved.

(2) Possibly a meeting of those involved.

(3) Consideration of relevant documentation.

FIRST REPORT AVAILABLE WITHIN **30 WORKING DAYS** OF PANEL BEING FINALLY ESTABLISHED

FINAL REPORT SHOULD BE SENT TO THE COMPLAIN-ANT **15 WORKING DAYS** AFTER DRAFT REPORT

AIM: TO COMPLETE THE INDEPENDENT REVIEW STAGE WITHIN **THREE MONTHS** OF COMPLAINANT CONTACTING THE CONVENOR

SECTION 2: GENERAL MEDICAL COUNCIL

INTRODUCTION

2–60 The General Medical Council ("GMC") is a council of doctors and lay members, *i.e.* non-doctors. There are 104 members, including 25 lay members who represent the public. The remaining 79 are doctors from all specialities.

2–61 The main purpose of the GMC is to "protect patients and guide doctors". The medical profession is self-regulating and thus the council seeks to assist it in maintaining good practice by promoting effective self-regulation. This is achieved in a number of ways:

(i) Monitoring the quality of doctors' training.

(ii) Maintaining a register of qualified doctors including checking doctors' qualifications. It should be noted that the right or licence to practice is conferred on doctors by the council on registration, and a doctor who is not registered is not entitled to practice medicine in the United Kingdom.

(iii) Publishing guidance on the standards of practice expected of registered doctors.

(iv) Investigating complaints about a doctor's conduct or competence.

2–62 It should be noted that registration is central to the council's ability to carry out its role of protecting the public and regulating the profession.

2–63 It is an offence for anyone to claim to be a registered medical practitioner if they are not registered with the GMC, however, at the time of writing, the letters after a doctor's name give no indication as to whether a doctor is registered or not. This situation should be contrasted with other health professionals, for example nurses and physiotherapists. It means that the only way to tell if a doctor is registered is to contact the council directly. The telephone number for inquiries regarding registration is 0171 915 3630.

GUIDELINES ON PROFESSIONAL PRACTICE

The GMC has recently taken a number of steps to ensure that **2–64** both doctors and patients have a better idea of the standards expected of doctors, and what procedures are in place to deal with complaints about a particular doctor's performance. To this end, the GMC consulted with a large number of patient representative groups at the beginning of 1997 and subsequently revised performance procedures, taking into account comments made by these groups. The council has also published guidelines on standards of competence and principles of good medical practice.

A doctor should: **2–65**

- Make care of the patient the first concern.
- Treat every patient politely and considerately.
- Respect patients' dignity and privacy.
- Listen to patients and respect their views.
- Give patients information in a way they can understand.
- Respect the rights of patients to be fully involved in discussions about their case.
- Keep professional knowledge and skills up to date.
- Recognise the limits of individual professional competence.
- Be honest and trustworthy.
- Respect and protect confidential information
- Ensure personal beliefs do not prejudice patients' care.
- Act quickly to protect patients at risk from a colleague who is not fit to practise.
- Avoid abusing his/her position as a doctor.
- Work with colleagues in the way that best serves the patient's interests.
- In all these matters doctors should never discriminate unfairly against patients or colleagues.
- Doctors should always be prepared to justify their actions to patients and colleagues.

COMPLAINTS PROCEDURE

2–66 Until very recently there were only a limited number of situations in which the council could investigate a doctor's fitness to practise, but its powers have now been extended by the Medical (Professional Performance) Act 1995. This has been seen to be possibly the most important extension of the GMC's powers since it was founded in 1858.

2–67 The new powers took effect from July 1, 1997 with new performance procedures being implemented in September 1997.

2–68 All complaints are handled in the same way at the initial investigation stage. The GMC describes this as "generic screening". The case is then referred to the correct procedure.

COMPLAINTS INVESTIGATED BY THE GMC

2–69 Despite the limits on the council's jurisdiction, a considerable variety of situations have been investigated over the last few years:

(i) alleged serious professional misconduct;

(ii) a doctor's health, either physical or mental, affecting his/her ability to practise;

(iii) a doctor having a certificate of conviction following a criminal offence. *N.B.* the police send these automatically to the GMC, a situation which should be contrasted with other health professionals whose convictions are not automatically reported to the regulatory body, for example the Council for Professions Supplementary to Medicine; and

(iv) a doctor's professional performance being "seriously deficient".

SERIOUS PROFESSIONAL MISCONDUCT

2–70 In the *Patients' Guide* to how the GMC handles complaints, the council does not define professional misconduct. In fact the expression "serious professional misconduct" was substituted by the Medical Act 1969 for the phrase "infamous conduct in a professional respect" which was used in the Medical Act 1858, *i.e.* the Act by which the council was set up.

Some guidance about the meaning of the phrase "infamous 2–71 conduct in a professional respect" can be found in the council's paper on disciplinary processes, where Lord Justice Lopes' definition in 1894 is set out:

"If a medical man in the pursuit of his profession has done something with regard to it which will be reasonably regarded as disgraceful or dishonourable by his professional brethren of good repute and competency, then it is up to the General Medical Council if that be shown, to say that he has been guilty of infamous conduct in a professional respect."

In another judgment delivered in 1930, Lord Justice Scrutton 2–72 stated that:

"Infamous conduct in a professional respect means no more than serious misconduct judged according to the rules, written or unwritten, governing the profession."

The GMC intended the phrase "serious professional misconduct" to have the same significance as its predecessor, "infamous conduct in a professional respect".

SERIOUSLY DEFICIENT PERFORMANCE

The Medical (Professional Performance) Act 1995 has extended 2–73 the powers of the GMC to enable the council to investigate cases where a doctor's standards of professional performance are seriously deficient, *i.e.* where a doctor is providing a generally poor standard of practice.

This is an important addition. Previously the GMC was not 2–74 able to sanction doctors who were simply not up to scratch, but only those guilty of serious professional misconduct, or those who were unfit to practise due to ill health. Also, serious professional misconduct has traditionally encompassed a huge range of issues, including gross rudeness and criminal behaviour, but not seriously deficient performance. It is important to the GMC's ability to provide effective self-regulation and is to be welcomed.

Seriously deficient performance is defined by the GMC as a 2–75 departure from good professional practice which is sufficiently serious to call into question the doctor's registration. This can

happen if there is a persistent failure to comply with professional standards appropriate to the work being carried out by
the doctor, especially if this poses a threat to patients' safety.

2–76   Seriously deficient performances may include, but not necessarily be confined to, persistent failure to comply with GMC
guidelines.

HOW COMPLAINTS ARE HANDLED

2–77 The GMC has three procedures for handling complaints; the
choice of procedure depends upon the nature of the complaint.
The GMC decides which procedure is appropriate upon receipt
of the complaint. The over-riding concern of the council in
making an assessment is the protection of patients and how best
this can be achieved.

2–78   The three procedures can operate independently of one
another, but there are occasions when a complaint can start
down one route and then be transferred to another procedure if
further evidence suggests this would be more appropriate.

2–79   The three types of procedure are as follows:

1. CONDUCT PROCEDURE

2–80 This procedure is used when the complaint is about serious
professional misconduct and/or relates to a criminal offence.
The question is whether the doctor should be allowed to
continue to practise medicine without restriction.

2. HEALTH PROCEDURE

2–81 This is used to handle complaints when there is evidence that
the doctor is seriously ill and illness makes him/her a danger to
patients or colleagues. This will almost certainly involve mental
illness or some form of addiction. The issue is whether the
doctor's health physical or mental, affects his/her fitness to
practise. This procedure is concerned with the general investigation of the doctor's health rather than with the particular
event(s) leading up to the complaint.

2–82   The process is also carried out with a view to obtaining
voluntary co-operation by the doctor, both in terms of answering
the complaint and persuading the doctor to take steps to
prevent the situation happening again or getting even worse, for
example seeking medical help.

3. PERFORMANCE PROCEDURE

This procedure is only used when a doctor's pattern of profes- **2–83**
sional performance is "seriously deficient". Detailed performance procedures have now been introduced.

TYPES OF COMPLAINT

- Rudeness to patients or colleagues.   **2–84**

- Criminal convictions such as drink-driving offences or,
  perhaps more seriously, sexual assault.

- Persistently poor performance, including poor operative
  results, leading to unnecessary complications or even death.

- Disregard of professional responsibility to patients.

- Altering/not making records.

- Financial dishonesty.

- Trafficking in human organs.

The list is much broader than this and is fairly wide-ranging.

TIME LIMIT

There is no time limit within which a complaint has to be **2–85**
lodged, although obviously the sooner after the event the better,
in that memories will be fresh and documentary evidence still
available. If too much time has elapsed, it can be difficult for the
council to investigate the complaint and for the parties to
remember what actually happened. Also, if the doctor is a
danger to other patients then the sooner something can be done
the better.

WHO CAN COMPLAIN

Complaints are received from a variety of sources.   **2–86**

- Members of the public, mostly patients or relatives.

- Professional colleagues.

- Police following criminal convictions.

- Health authorities/Trusts.

- Community health councils

27

HOW TO MAKE A COMPLAINT

2–87   1. All formal complaints should be made in writing to the Screening and Conduct section of the GMC. The address and telephone number are given at Appendix B.

2. The following information must be included.
(i) The full name and address of the doctor.
(ii) Precise details of what, in the complainant's view, the doctor has done or failed to do.
(iii) The date(s) when the event(s) occurred.
(iv) Copies of any relevant papers and any other documentary evidence, *e.g.* photographs, tape recordings, police reports or investigation number.
(v) The name and address of anyone who either witnessed the events or has personal knowledge and can testify to those events.

2–89   The GMC actually publishes a form which can be used when making a complaint, a copy of which can be found at the end of this Chapter. If the form is used or the format adopted, it will ensure that the complainant covers all of the relevant points and gives as much information as is required for the complaint to be addressed.

2–90   *N.B.* Any doctor or individual member of the public submitting a formal complaint which is to be taken further after initial assessment will be asked to include the information at numbers (i) to (v) above, in a statutory declaration, which is a statement made on oath that has to be sworn in the presence of a solicitor, a Notary Public or a Commissioner for Oaths.

2–91   The documentation is considered and then passed to the relevant section of the Performance division or the Fitness to Practice division. If the papers are in order, they are then forwarded to those responsible for the first stage of the investigation process.

2–92   There follows an initial generic assessment which is common to all complaints, the purpose of which is to decide which procedural route is appropriate given the circumstances of the complaint. This does not apply to the police, health authorities, community health councils or employers, etc.

ALL COMPLAINTS

INITIAL SCREENING PROCESS

All complaints about a doctor's conduct and performance will **2–93** be dealt with initially in the same way. They will be referred to one of a team of medical members of the GMC appointed as "screeners".

The screener will consider the complaint with particular **2–94** regard to the following:

- The seriousness of the matter.

- Any other information which the council may have received about the same doctor.

- Any evidence that the complainant has been able to provide in support of the complaint.

N.B. No complaint is ever rejected at the screening stage unless **2–95** at least two GMC members have seen it. One of those will be a lay member whose specific task is to look at the complaints from the patient's point of view. If that lay member feels that the GMC should take the complaint further then it will do so.

SCREENING PROCEDURE

- The complaint is assessed by the preliminary screener and/ **2–96** or a lay member of the council.

- The complainant is asked for permission to let the doctor **2–97** see a copy of the complaint. If the complainant refuses then the complaint will not be taken further and the file is closed.

- In many cases the screener(s) may require advice from one **2–98** or more experts in the speciality in which the doctor has been working, before making a decision as to whether the GMC should act. This advice can come from other members of the GMC with expertise in the relevant speciality. In addition the Royal Colleges or relevant professional associations may be requested to nominate specialists ad hoc to advise the screener(s) in individual cases.

- In cases involving complaints about conduct or perfor- **2–99** mance, the screener(s) will normally want to establish whether any action has already been taken by another body or authority, for example employers under NHS disciplinary procedures, or whether the complainant has already instigated the complaint using the NHS complaints procedure. It may be that GMC action should continue or will be postponed until the other investigation has been concluded.

2–100   ● In cases involving a complaint about a doctor's performance, then the doctor will receive a letter inviting preliminary comments on the complaint before the screener(s) will make a final decision.

2–101   ● If the screener decides that the GMC should act, then the complainant is asked for a sworn written statement in support of the complaint (but only if the complainant is a member of the public or another doctor). The complainant may also be asked for written statements from other people with personal knowledge of the event—these need not be sworn statements.

2–102   ● Also in relation to performance procedures, a doctor may be requested to undergo assessment, but only if the lay screener(s) agrees that no further action should be taken under the conduct rules. That leaves only two options, referral to performance procedures or no action. If it is not a conduct matter and the medical screener asks for the doctor to go for a performance assessment then the matter is automatically referred to the performance procedures.

2–103   ● It is obviously sometimes difficult to prepare formal statements and the GMC is prepared to consider paying legal costs associated with the drafting of the complainant's statement and any witness statements.

2–104   ● If, following this initial assessment of both sides' evidence, the screener(s) and the lay member decide that the case will not be taken further, then the file will be closed.

2–105   ● The complainant will be informed of any decision made by the screener(s).

POSSIBLE OUTCOMES OF THE SCREENING PROCESS

(a) REJECTION OF THE COMPLAINT

The following complaints are unlikely to be investigated: **2–106**

- Complaints that are not sufficiently serious to warrant reviewing the doctor's registration.

- Complaints which do not relate to an identifiable doctor.

- Complaints for which there is insufficient evidence.

- Complaints which have no bearing on a doctor's practice.

- Complaints made anonymously.

(b) CASE REFERRED TO THE HEALTH SCREENER

This happens when further inquiries reveal that the doctor's **2–107** alleged misconduct or poor performance was probably caused by serious ill health.

(c) DOCTOR IS REFERRED FOR ASSESSMENT

This will occur if the complaint is regarding the doctor's **2–108** performance.

(d) THE CASE IS REFERRED TO THE CONDUCT PROCEDURES

The screener may decide to refer the matter to the preliminary **2–109** proceedings committee.

HEALTH PROCEDURES

AIM OF THE PROCEDURES

The procedures are designed for the following purposes: **2–110**

(a) To protect patients.

(b) To provide continued monitoring of the care of sick doctors with the aim of returning them to unrestricted practice.

(c) To treat cases of sick doctors with the same confidentiality as those of patients.

31

2–111 The health procedures involve four main stages:

STAGE I: Preliminary consideration of evidence
STAGE II: Medical examination
STAGE III: Medical supervision and rehabilitation of a sick doctor
STAGE IV: The Health Committee

These are all carried out by the Health Screeners.

Stage I—Initial Assessment

2–112 The investigation is carried out with a view to obtaining voluntary co-operation by the doctor, both in terms of answering the complaint and persuading the doctor to take steps to prevent the situation from happening again, or getting even worse—or example, seeking medical help.

2–113 The Council only intervenes if the voluntary arrangements break down and will only allow a doctor suffering from serious ill health to carry on practising medicine when it is safe to do so and under appropriate supervision.

Stage II—Medical Examination

2–114 If the screener(s) are satisfied that further action is necessary then the doctor is invited to be medically examined by at least two medical examiners chosen by the screener from panels nominated by professional bodies, including Royal Colleges and the British Medical Association (BMA).

2–115 These medical examiners must report on whether the doctor is fit to practise without restriction, or if not, what steps need to be taken to get the doctor back to full health. The examiner's report is sent to the doctor as well as the GMC. The doctor may be asked to accept supervision or accept voluntary restrictions on practice, for example he/she may have to agree not to practise single-handedly or to refrain from practice for the foreseeable future.

Stage III—Medical Supervision

2–116 If the medical examiners recommend that the doctor be supervised, then the medical supervisor provides or arranges any necessary treatment and reports periodically to the screener on the doctor's progress. On the basis of these reports, the screener(s) may review any limitations on the doctor's practice, and if good practice is maintained those limitations may gradually be removed until the doctor is able to return to unrestricted practice without supervision.

Stage IV—The Health Committee
Cases are only referred to the health committee in the following **2–117** circumstances:

(i) A doctor fails to co-operate with medical examination or refuses to be put under medical supervision.

(ii) A doctor reneges on an agreement to follow the medical examiner's recommendation.

(iii) A doctor suffers a deterioration in ill health.

The question of the doctor's health arises during the course of disciplinary proceedings when the matter will be referred to the health committee by the disciplinary committee.

STRUCTURE OF THE HEALTH COMMITTEE

The health committee is elected annually by the GMC from **2–118** amongst its members. Membership comprises:

- the chairman;
- five other medical members; and
- two lay members.

In addition, the committee is advised by specialist medical assessors chosen by the preliminary screener from panels nominated by professional bodies.

PROCEDURE

1. The committee is assisted at hearings by a legal assessor **2–119** who advises on points of law.

2. The committee meets in private.

3. Hearings are not adversarial.

4. The doctor is entitled to be legally represented.

5. The doctor may require attendance of witnesses for cross-examination.

6. The principal evidence is usually written medical reports.

All papers are sent beforehand to the doctor and committee members for review prior to the hearing.

POSSIBLE DECISIONS OF THE HEALTH COMMITTEE

(a) The Doctor is fit to practise
2–120   In this case the complaint or investigation will be completed and the doctor and any complainant will be informed of the outcome.

(b) Conditions imposed upon registration
2–121   ● If the committee finds the doctor's fitness to practise to be seriously impaired, it may impose conditions upon the doctor's registration for up to *three years* and thereafter up to *12 months*. After the period given, the case will be referred back to the health committee which will review whether or not the doctor's health has improved sufficiently for him or her to resume practice unsupervised, or whether a further period of supervision or treatment is necessary.

2–122   ● One of the conditions will always include the requirement to accept medical supervision and may also include restrictions on a doctor's professional practice if that is necessary to protect patients, and/or the doctor's own health.

(c) Suspension from the register
2–123   The committee has the power to suspend registration for up to *12 months*, but again once that period has expired, the case will be referred back to the health committee which must reconsider whether the suspension is still justified.

(d) Indefinite suspension
2–124   In cases where the doctor's registration has been suspended for two years or more, the committee has the power to impose indefinite suspension.

APPEAL

The doctor can appeal against a decision of the health com- **2–125**
mittee to the Judicial Committee of the Privy Council. An
appeal can be made only on a question of law.

CONDUCT PROCEDURES

If the complaint is about a doctor's conduct and the screener(s) **2–126**
raises a potential issue of serious professional misconduct, that
is dealt with by way of the conduct procedures.

There are two committees set up to deal with complaints **2–127**
about a doctor's conduct.

1. Preliminary Proceedings Committee

2. Professional Conduct Committee

PRELIMINARY PROCEEDINGS COMMITTEE

The Preliminary Proceedings Committee ("PPC") consists of **2–128**
seven members, five of whom are medical members and two of
whom are lay members. It is elected annually by the General
Medical Council.

If the complaint is about a doctor's conduct and the screener **2–129**
decides that it should be investigated further, the complaint will
be referred to the PPC.

PROCEDURE

1. The preliminary proceedings committee will review all the **2–130**
   papers in the case, including the original complaint, any
   documentation in support, and the doctor's response.

2. If from the papers a question of serious professional **2–131**
   misconduct does arise, but the evidence initially received is
   insufficient or does not correspond to the rules, the GMC
   solicitor may make further inquiries or seek additional
   documentation. If after these further inquiries, it is likely
   that the case will or will not proceed to the PPC, then either
   the President of the GMC or a medical member of the
   GMC must be consulted.

3. Interestingly, if the matter is not going to proceed then the **2–132**
   President and a lay member must be consulted.

35

2–133 4. Neither the complainant nor the doctor has to attend to the PPC meeting, which is held in private.

2–134 5. Both the complainant and the doctor will receive a letter saying what action the PPC has decided to take.

POWERS OF THE PRELIMINARY PROCEEDINGS COMMITTEE

2–135 After considering the evidence, the committee can:

(a) Decide no further action is justified
2–136 This is because there is insufficient evidence or it is clear from the papers that the matter is not concerned with serious professional misconduct.

(b) Send the doctor a letter of advice or warning
2–137 This is in less serious cases where the committee feels that the doctor's conduct was perhaps not as good as it should have been, but does not amount to serious professional misconduct. This will end the matter.

(c) Referral to the Health or Professional Performance Procedures
2–138 This will only arise if following investigation by the PPC it is clear that the conduct has arisen due to the doctor's ill health or that the issue is not really one of conduct but of competence.

(d) Interim Conditional Registration
2–139 ● If the PPC decides to refer a case either to the professional conduct committee or to the health committee, it may make an order imposing conditions upon the doctor's continuing registration. Such an order is only intended to be effective until the case has been considered by the professional conduct committee or the health committee.

● No such order can be made unless the doctor has been offered the opportunity to appear before the PPC and be heard on the question of whether such an order is appropriate.

● For this purpose the doctor may be legally represented.

● An order can be made initially for a period of up to *six months*.

- A conditional order will only be made if it is necessary to protect the public or if it is in the doctor's best interests.

(e) Interim Suspension

If the PPC decides to refer a case either to the Professional **2–140** Conduct Committee or to the Health Committee, it may make an order suspending the doctor with immediate effect. Such an order is only intended to be effective until the case has been considered by the Professional Conduct Committee or the Health Committee.

- No such order can be made unless the doctor has been **2–141** offered the opportunity to appear before the PPC and be heard on the question of whether such an order is appropriate.

- For this purpose the doctor may be legally represented.

- An order can be made initially for a period of up to *six months*.

- An immediate suspension order will only be made if it is necessary to protect the public or is in the doctor's best interests.

PROFESSIONAL CONDUCT COMMITTEE

The Professional Conduct Committee ("PCC") investigates **2–142** complaints concerning serious professional misconduct that have been referred by the PPC.

PROCEDURE

1. The PCC carries out its initial investigation based on the **2–143** papers and documentary evidence already submitted.

2. Both sides may be required to give additional evidence and **2–144** if the doctor has yet to provide a written response to the complaint then he or she will be asked to do so.

3. If a doctor has been convicted of a criminal offence, then **2–145** the PCC must accept as conclusive evidence the guilt of the doctor. In these cases, the proceedings are only concerned to establish the gravity of the offence and to take account of any mitigating circumstances.

2–146 4. The meetings are held in public.

2–147 5. The PCC must determine whether the facts are proven to their satisfaction. In practice this means that the burden is higher than the "balance of probabilities" though usually not "beyond reasonable doubt".

2–148 6. The PCC is advised on the question of law by a legal assessor who is usually a Q.C., and must be a barrister, advocate or solicitor of not less than 10 years' qualification.

2–149 7. The PCC is elected annually by the Council and consists of 30 members of whom up to eight sit on any case. Of the 30 members, 23 are medical members of the GMC and several are lay members.

2–150 8. The procedure is very similar to that of a court of law.

2–151 9. Witnesses may be subpoenaed.

2–152 10. Evidence is given on oath.

2–153 11. Doctors who appear before the committee are usually legally represented.

2–154 12. The complainant will be required to give oral evidence on oath, as in court proceedings and may be questioned by the committee and the lawyer defending the case.

2–155 Complainants may be represented by a lawyer or present the case in person. If legal representation is sought then the GMC may agree to pay any reasonable legal expenses. *N.B.* Legal aid is not available for complaints.

POWERS OF THE PROFESSIONAL CONDUCT COMMITTEE

2–156 At the conclusion of an inquiry the committee can:

(a) Dismiss the case
2–157 If the PCC considers that there is insufficient evidence of serious professional misconduct then the matter will be dismissed.

(b) Public Inquiry
2–158 The PCC can refer a matter for public inquiry if it is sufficiently serious or of public importance.

(c) Postpone a decision

- This occurs when the PCC would like to have further **2–159** information or would like to monitor the doctor's progress during the period of postponement to see whether there is an improvement.

- During the period of postponement the doctor's name **2–160** remains on the register.

- The doctor will have to provide names of professional **2–161** colleagues who will be able to supply information about his/her conduct during the period of postponement to be submitted to members of the PCC at the resumed hearing which will take place after the period of postponement.

- The replies received from these professional colleagues, as **2–162** well as any other information submitted by the doctor, will be taken into account at the resumed hearing.

- If the information is satisfactory then the case will be **2–163** concluded.

- If, however, there would appear to be further problems with **2–164** the doctor's behaviour, then the determination may be postponed for a further period, or the committee may direct suspension or erasure, or impose conditions on the doctor's registration.

(d) Conditions Imposed on registration

- Conditions can only be imposed for a specified period, after **2–165** which a resumed hearing will take place.

- If the doctor has complied with the conditions then the **2 166** conditions can be removed and the case will be concluded.

- On the other hand, if the doctor has failed to comply with **2–167** the conditions, the committee may direct suspension of the doctor's registration or erasure of the doctor's name from the register.

- Examples of conditions which may be imposed include that **2–168** a doctor should not engage in specified branches of medical practice or any practice when not supervised, or should not prescribe, possess or control drugs.

(e) Suspension of registration

The Committee can order the suspension of the doctor's **2–169** registration for up to a maximum of *one year*.

2–170   ● Again, the doctor will be asked to provide names of professional colleagues who will be asked to provide evidence at the resumed hearing as to whether or not the doctor should still be suspended.

2–171   ● If the doctor's conduct in the period of suspension is acceptable, then the case will be concluded.

2–172   ● If at the resumed hearing the evidence would seem to suggest that the doctor's conduct is still not acceptable, then the committee can recommend further suspension or erasure of the doctor's name from the register.

(f) Removal of a doctor's name from the register

2–173 This would only take place in the most serious cases. Whereas suspension can only be ordered for a specified period, erasure remains effective unless and until the doctor makes a successful application for restoration to the register. Such an application for restoration can only be made *10 months* after the original took effect.

APPEALS

2–174 1. A doctor has a right of appeal to the Judicial Committee of the Privy Council following removal of his/her name from the register.

2–175 2. If there is an appeal, the complainant will not be asked to appear at the appeal hearing and may not be told that an appeal has been made, and so if the complainant wishes to know whether or not an appeal has been made, he/she will have to contact the GMC after the PCC hearing.

2–176 3. An appeal must be made within *28 days* of an order that the doctor's name be erased from the register or that registration will be suspended or subject to conditions.

2–177 4. During the period between the notice of appeal and the appeal, the doctor's registration remains unaffected unless the PCC has made a separate order that the doctor's registration shall be immediately suspended in the interests of protecting the public.

2–178 5. There is a right of appeal against an order for immediate suspension to the High Court, but this in no way affects the doctor's right to appeal to the Judicial Committee of the

Privy Council respecting an order for removal of his/her name from the register or conditions or suspension from the register.

RESTORATION TO THE REGISTER

1. Such an application can only be made *10 months* or more **2–179** after the date of removal from the register.

2. Such applications are made to the PCC.

3. A hearing will take place at which the applicant may appear in person.

4. The committee considers every application on its merits having regard to, *inter alia*, the nature and seriousness of the original offence and the doctor's conduct in the intervening period.

5. If the application is unsuccessful then a further period of at least *10 months* must elapse before another application can be made.

PERFORMANCE PROCEDURE

There are two committees involved in investigating professional **2–180** performance.

1. Assessment Referral Committee

2. Committee on Professional Performance

The procedure in relation to professional performance is in four stages.

Stage I—Initial Assessment

This is a stage common to all of the GMC's complaints **2–181** procedures. The following aspects of the initial screening process for performance procedures are slightly different to the others:

1. The screener will wish to establish whether or not the **2–182** complaint is being dealt with by way of another avenue, for example whether disciplinary proceedings have been instituted by the employer or whether a patient has instigated the NHS complaints procedures. If so, then the GMC

41

will decide whether or not to proceed with the complaint or delay until the relevant authority has concluded its investigation.

2–183 2. The doctor will receive a letter inviting preliminary comments on the complaint before a screener reaches the final decision.

2–184 3. The doctor may be asked to undergo an assessment of performance.

Stage II—Assessment of Performance

2–185 An assessment will take place either because a screener has asked the doctor to submit to an assessment, and the doctor has complied with the request, or in the event that the doctor refuses, by way of a referral from the Assessment Referral Committee ("ARC").

2–186 Once a decision has been made to refer a doctor for assessment then a case co-ordinator will take over the management of each case from the preliminary screener. Case co-ordinators will be medically qualified GMC members appointed by the GMC to direct/manage cases referred into the performance procedures.

Assessment Panels

2–187 These are panels especially set up to carry out assessments of the doctor's performance. They consist of two medically qualified assessors drawn from lists of appointed specialists. One of the two medically qualified assessors—the lead assessor—will be an experienced assessor in the same general speciality as the doctor being assessed. The other will be a peer from the same sub-speciality.

2–188 In selecting assessors for individual cases, the GMC is keen to stress that the gender and ethnic background of the doctor will be taken into consideration where possible. A lay person will also be appointed to the assessment panel in each case. Assessors are sent information about each case including a copy of the original complaint, the doctor's preliminary comments and any further evidence that the doctor or complainant wishes to provide.

Assessment Procedure

2–189 The content of each assessment will be tailored so that it is appropriate for the speciality of the doctor being assessed and reflects the nature of the practice he/she undertakes. However, all assessments will follow the same basic structure, which is likely to include:

- A visit to the doctor's place of practice.

- Review of the doctor's clinical records.

- An interview with the doctor.

- Exploration of the doctor's clinical reasoning and experience.

- Inquiries of third parties, or professional colleagues with direct knowledge of the doctor's performance.

- Questions or tasks designed to assess the doctor's clinical knowledge, skills and attitudes.

Following the assessment, the assessors will submit a report **2–190** containing a profile of the doctor's performance and will offer opinions regarding any measures which might be appropriate to remedy deficiencies in the doctor's performance to protect the public.

A doctor may refuse to co-operate with the assessment **2–191** procedures, in which case he/she will be referred to the Committee on Professional Performance ("CPP"), or he/she may decide to comply with the assessment or to retire from practice voluntarily.

Stage III—Remedial Action and Re-Assessment

- The assessor's report is sent to the doctor for comment.   **2–192**

- The doctor's comments and the assessor's report are then **2–193** sent to the case co-ordinator.

- Once the case co-ordinator has seen the report and the **2–194** doctor's comments on it, he/she decides what medial action is required. This may include requiring the doctor to sign up to a "statement of requirements" concerning remedial treatment. *N.B.* This is a statement of requirements *not* recommendations.

- If the assessment has revealed the doctor's performance to **2–195** be so seriously deficient as to put patients at risk, the case co-ordinator will refer the case direct to the CPP to consider appropriate action (*e.g.* formal sanctions on registration). In these circumstances, the case co-ordinator's "statement of requirements" route will not apply.

2–196 • In making decisions, the case co-ordinators have to follow criteria established by the CPP, and it is that committee which will audit the case co-ordinator's work.

2–197 • A copy of the assessor's report is sent to the doctor along with the case co-ordinator's recommendations. The doctor is invited to comply with the case co-ordinator's recommendations and the GMC encourages the doctor to arrange a meeting with the case co-ordinator so that the recommendations can be explained and discussed.

2–198 • If the question of professional performance is actually related to the ill health of the doctor, then the aim will usually be to obtain the doctor's co-operation and voluntary undertaking to take whatever steps are necessary to regain his/her health.

2–199 • After an initial period of remedial action a re-assessment will be undertaken.

2–200 • If it appears that the remedial action has been successful, the case will be concluded, but only if the case co-ordinator and lay adviser agree. However, if the initial period of remedial action does not appear to have achieved significant benefit then the doctor's case will be referred to CPP.

2–201 • If further remedial action is required then this will be suggested, with a further re-assessment to take place at the end of that remedial action.

2–202 • If the doctor refuses to comply with the case co-ordinator's suggestions or the assessment panel finds that there are serious performance problems, then the matter will be referred to the CPP.

Stage IV—Committee on Professional Performance

2–203 Cases are referred either by the preliminary screener(s) and/or the case co-ordinator in the following circumstances:

(i) where the doctor fails to undergo assessment, having agreed to do so as the direction of the screener(s), or having been directed to do so by the ARC;

(ii) where the case co-ordinator does not accept the opinion of the assessment panel in their report;

(iii) upon assessment the doctor's performance is judged to be so poor as to present a serious risk to patients;

(iv) where having undergone assessment, the doctor refuses to agree to the requirements for further action devised by the case co-ordinator;

(v) where, having agreed to those requirements, the doctor fails to comply with them;

(vi) where the doctor's performance fails to improve significantly after he/she has taken the recommended remedial action; or

(vii) where the doctor in any other way fails to co-operate with the procedure.

Purpose of the Committee on Professional Performance
The function of this committee is to determine whether the **2–204** standard of the doctor's professional performance has been seriously deficient.

Procedure
1. Meetings are held in private unless the doctor himself/ **2–205** herself actually requests a public hearing.

2. The doctor and the complainant in the case have the right to be present.

3. Both parties can be legally represented.

4. It should be noted that again, legal aid will not be available for the complainant.

5. The CPP will be assisted by one or more independent specialist advisers for each case.

6. The GMC will publish findings of serious deficient performance by the Professional Performance Committee.

7. Details of individual assessments will not be made available to the public.

8. Reports will be published annually describing a selection of cases and the results.

Powers of the Committee on Professional Performance

2–206 In cases where sanctions are imposed, the hearing will be resumed after a given time interval, at which point further sanctions can be imposed or the case may be concluded.

(a) Conditions imposed on registration

2–207 These are basically the same as those of the health committee, including powers to impose conditions on a doctor's registration.

(b) Suspension of registration

2–208 These are basically the same as those of the health committee including the power to suspend doctor's registration. After a suspension of registration for at least *two years* the Committee can recommend indefinite suspension and registration may only be resumed if the doctor requests a review.

CONCLUSION

2–209 The GMC complaints procedures have recently undergone an overhaul and are now more comprehensive. The extension of the GMC's jurisdiction to cover seriously deficient performance is to be welcomed.

Following this extension it would possibly be appropriate for cases involving medical negligence, where judgment is entered against the doctor, to be referred automatically to the GMC.

2–210 The GMC publishes a number of helpful leaflets for doctors and patients who wish to know more about the procedures. These are available from the GMC—see Appendix B. However, the GMC does not appear to have a comprehensive guide to the complaints process, which can make it difficult for someone who wishes to complain to find the information which is relevant to his/her situation. For the GMC form on which patients may make a formal complaint, see the end of this chapter.

DOCTORS — SIMPLIFIED SCHEMATIC OF THE GMC COMPLAINTS PROCEDURES

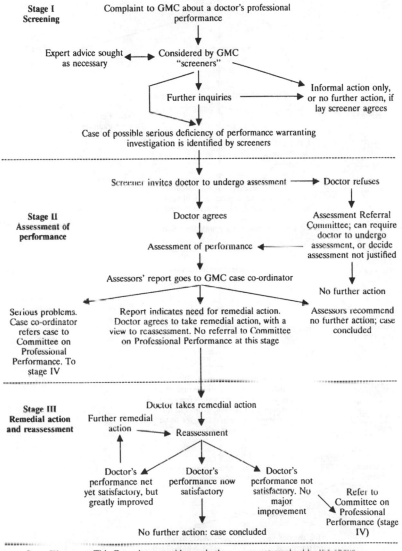

Stage I Screening

Complaint to GMC about a doctor's professional performance

Expert advice sought as necessary ⟷ Considered by GMC "screeners"

Further inquiries ⟶ Informal action only, or no further action, if lay screener agrees

Case of possible serious deficiency of performance warranting investigation is identified by screeners

Screener invites doctor to undergo assessment ⟶ Doctor refuses

Stage II Assessment of performance

Doctor agrees

Assessment of performance ⟵

Assessment Referral Committee; can require doctor to undergo assessment, or decide assessment not justified

Assessors' report goes to GMC case co-ordinator

No further action

Serious problems. Case co-ordinator refers case to Committee on Professional Performance. To stage IV

Report indicates need for remedial action. Doctor agrees to take remedial action, with a view to reassessment. No referral to Committee on Professional Performance at this stage

Assessors recommend no further action; case concluded

Stage III Remedial action and reassessment

Doctor takes remedial action

Further remedial action ⟶ Reassessment

Doctor's performance not yet satisfactory, but greatly improved

Doctor's performance now satisfactory

Doctor's performance not satisfactory. No major improvement

Refer to Committee on Professional Performance (stage IV)

No further action: case concluded

Stage IV Committee on Professional Performance

This Committee considers only those cases not resolved by the above procedures; for example, where the doctor does not co-operate with assessment or follow the recommendations for remedial action, or doctor's performance does not improve after remedial action, or the doctor is advised to retire, but refuses to do so.

47

Stage I: Screening

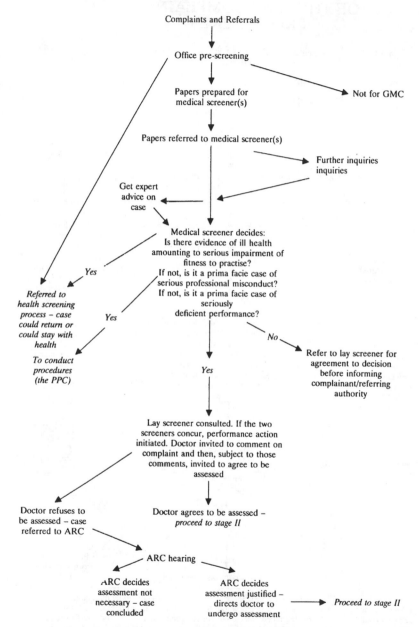

Stage II: Assessment of performance

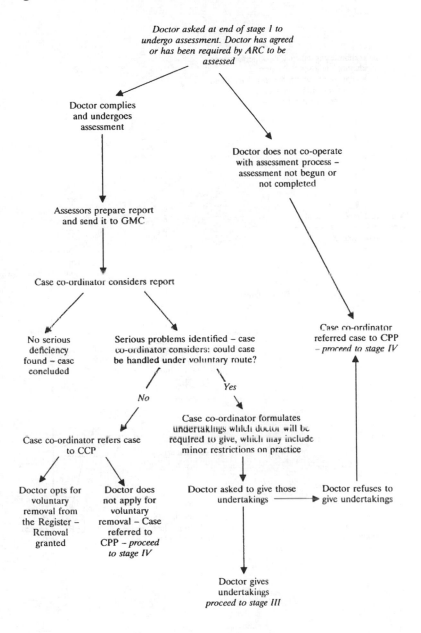

Doctor asked at end of stage 1 to undergo assessment. Doctor has agreed or has been required by ARC to be assessed

Doctor complies and undergoes assessment

Doctor does not co-operate with assessment process – assessment not begun or not completed

Assessors prepare report and send it to GMC

Case co-ordinator considers report

No serious deficiency found – case concluded

Serious problems identified – case co-ordinator considers: could case be handled under voluntary route?

Case co-ordinator referred case to CPP – *proceed to stage IV*

No

Yes

Case co-ordinator refers case to CCP

Case co-ordinator formulates undertakings which doctor will be required to give, which may include minor restrictions on practice

Doctor opts for voluntary removal from the Register – Removal granted

Doctor does not apply for voluntary removal – Case referred to CPP – *proceed to stage IV*

Doctor asked to give those undertakings ⟶ Doctor refuses to give undertakings

Doctor gives undertakings *proceed to stage III*

49

Stage III: Rehabilitation and Reassessment

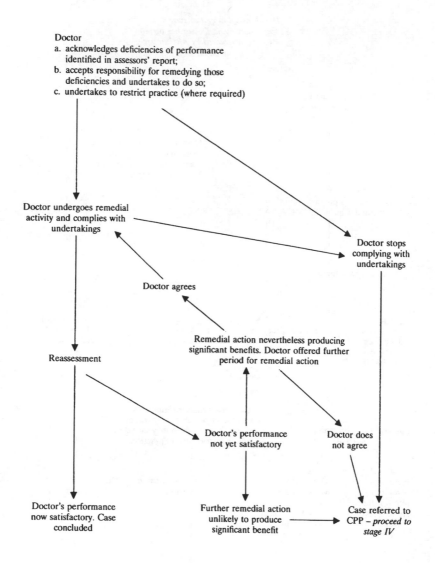

Doctor
a. acknowledges deficiencies of performance identified in assessors' report;
b. accepts responsibility for remedying those deficiencies and undertakes to do so;
c. undertakes to restrict practice (where required)

Doctor undergoes remedial activity and complies with undertakings

Doctor stops complying with undertakings

Doctor agrees

Remedial action nevertheless producing significant benefits. Doctor offered further period for remedial action

Reassessment

Doctor's performance not yet satisfactory

Doctor does not agree

Doctor's performance now satisfactory. Case concluded

Further remedial action unlikely to produce significant benefit

Case referred to CPP – *proceed to stage IV*

Stage IV: The Committee on Professional Performance

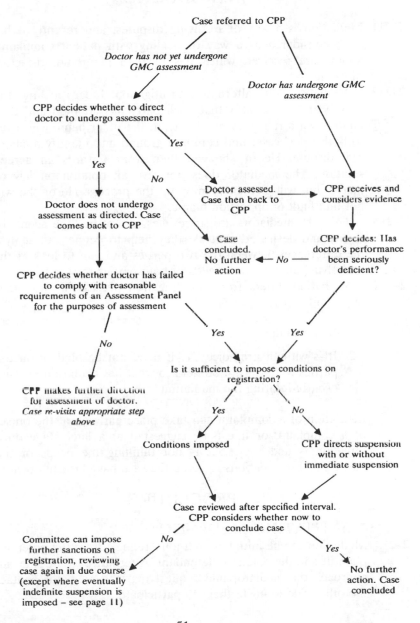

Case referred to CPP

Doctor has not yet undergone GMC assessment

Doctor has undergone GMC assessment

CPP decides whether to direct doctor to undergo assessment

Yes

Yes

No

Doctor does not undergo assessment as directed. Case comes back to CPP

Doctor assessed. Case then back to CPP

CPP receives and considers evidence

Case concluded. No further action ← *No* —

CPP decides: Has doctor's performance been seriously deficient?

CPP decides whether doctor has failed to comply with reasonable requirements of an Assessment Panel for the purposes of assessment

No

Yes

Yes

CPP makes further direction for assessment of doctor. *Case re-visits appropriate step above*

Is it sufficient to impose conditions on registration?

Yes

No

Conditions imposed

CPP directs suspension with or without immediate suspension

Case reviewed after specified interval. CPP considers whether now to conclude case

Committee can impose further sanctions on registration, reviewing case again in due course (except where eventually indefinite suspension is imposed – see page 11)

No

Yes

No further action. Case concluded

SECTION 3: MEDIATION OF COMPLAINTS REGARDING DOCTORS/NURSES

INTRODUCTION

2–211 Mediation is a way of resolving disputes, and recently it has been considered as a way of dealing with patient complaints about care received which has resulted in an unsatisfactory outcome.

2–212 Mediation is an alternative to litigation. Judges in litigation only hear the *positions* that each party has adopted and then hand down a ruling. A mediator, on the other hand, will listen to both sides' case, find common ground and identify areas of real dispute. He or she will then work towards an agreed solution. The mediator does not give an opinion on law or merits, but will give an opinion on the process. He or she will not find fault or apportion blame.

2–213 This why mediators are sometimes said to be "the agents of reality and devil's advocates"; they help to define and analyse the differences between the two parties and aim to look at the underlying interests and needs of both parties.

2–214 Mediation differs from the litigation process in two other important ways.

1. It is voluntary.

2. It is without prejudice, *i.e.* it need not be binding on the parties who will not be held to what has been said or what occurred during the mediation.

Mediation of a complaint can take place early on at the outset of a complaint, or it can be suggested at a later stage once litigation is underway, but is not fulfilling the needs of the parties, and negotiations to settle the case have broken down.

PROCEDURE

1. INITIATING MEDIATION

2–215 Mediation can be initiated on a joint request from the potential plaintiff and the potential defendant. Alternatively, one side can approach the mediator and request that the mediator contact the other side to invite them to participate.

2. TIMESCALES

As a general rule, mediations can be set up within *four to six* **2–216** *weeks* of being requested. It is necessary to obtain all the "available" dates for those whose presence is required, *e.g.* consultants, midwives, Trust claims managers, etc.

Once a date has been agreed, any documents and written submissions that the parties want the mediator to review prior to the mediation must be disclosed *two weeks* in advance of the meeting.

3. APPOINTMENT OF A MEDIATOR

The whole point of mediation is that the parties all meet in the **2–217** presence of a mediator. It is important that this is someone who has the relevant skills and has been properly trained for the task.

Organisations such as the Centre for Dispute Resolution **2–218** ("CEDR") or Alternative Dispute Resolution ("ADR") can assist by considering the particular dispute to be mediated, advising the parties on a suitable mediator and arranging the meeting.

Both organisations have a panel of accredited mediators, all **2–219** of whom have undergone a five day training course, at the end of which they are examined and their skills assessed. Once passed, the mediator must take part in two mediations under the supervision of a more experienced mediator, before he or she will be considered fully trained and competent to carry out their own mediation.

The mediators are people from various different backgrounds, **2–220** *e.g.* medical staff, counsellors, businessmen and women, etc, who have suitable experience to mediate on the issues at hand.

4. VENUE

Several organisations specialising in alternative dispute **2–221** resolution are able to organise an independent venue anywhere in the country. Commonly, the mediation takes place at the offices of one or other of the solicitors involved. It is necessary to have the use of three rooms: one main meeting room and two "breakout" rooms where each party can discuss their case privately.

5. ORGANISATION OF THE MEDIATION

The mediator will have prepared himself/herself for the **2–222** meeting. The day will start with a joint session during which both sides give a 15 or 20 minute presentation summarising how they see their side of the complaint. Thereafter, it is the mediator's job to focus the parties on the specific areas of dispute, and the issues that are of particular importance to both sides. In doing so the mediator will take on board the attitude and demeanour of both parties, and a lot would depend on their approach.

2–223   The mediator then talks with both sides independently and confidentially in the breakout rooms and undertakes what could be described as "shuttlecock" diplomacy.

2–224   CEDR recommend that both parties attend the joint meeting, since in their view the benefits of the parties facing each other and vocalising grievances should not be underestimated and is often a very constructive way to begin useful discussions.

6. PARTICIPANTS IN THE MEDIATION

2–225 Clearly, it is for the complainant to decide who he or she would like to be present from the other side. This is the complainant's chance to ask all the questions that he or she feels have not been answered so far.

2–226   Whilst it is not possible to *force* the Trust to bring a particular person, doctor, consultant or nurse to the mediation, it would be possible for the complainant to make the attendance of various people a pre-condition of the meeting.

2–227   Likewise the Trust may have certain requests in relation to people that they specifically want to be present.

2–228   Often, the partner goes with the complainant to the mediation, which is very important since the partner is often affected by the experience as well and feels that his or her voice needs to be heard in addition to the actual complainant.

7. DECISION

2–229 It is not the mediator's job to reach a judgment, but merely to facilitate discussions and encourage parties to reach common ground. Part of this discussion includes exploring the possibility of settlement or payment of compensation, so that the parties dispassionately review the advantages and disadvantages of resolution at this stage.

2–230   If the mediator is unable successfully to bring the parties to agreement, he or she can, on request, provide a written report about his or her view on reasonable settlement terms. Both parties can disregard the written report if they so wish.

The conclusion of any mediation is *non-binding*, which means 2–231 that should the recommendations for settlement not be to the complainant's satisfaction, he or she can then proceed to litigation. If, however, the settlement terms agreed at the mediation *are* acceptable to both parties, these terms are committed to writing on that day and a formal contract is formed.

8. COSTS

The way that costs are dealt with depends on the agreement 2–232 reached between both parties before the mediation process starts. Under normal circumstances both sides are responsible for their own costs. These are calculated on a per party/per day basis. The mediation service considers that this arrangement is psychologically advantageous, since then each side has a financial interest in resolving their difficulties quickly and efficiently. It is quite common, however, for agreement to be reached that the more financially able party (which in most cases is the potential defendant), should pay the costs of both sides. It can also be agreed that the defendants should also be liable for the costs up to and including the mediation.

The costs are calculated on a sliding scale dependent on the 2–233 value of the claim. At the time of writing, for a claim of up to £20,000, the charge is approximately £350 per party per day. For claims between £20,000 and £35,000 the charge is approximately £400 per party per day.

This fee includes: 2–234

- Any preliminary meetings that are needed with the mediation service.

- All discussions and advice on the process of mediation.

- All advice on a suitable Mediator.

- One day of mediation.

This fee does not include: 2–235

- The mediator's expenses of the mediator, *e.g.*. travel,

- Room hire for the day.

- In addition, it does not include the cost of any preparation that the mediator has to do. Such preparation, which is often necessary in complex cases, is charged at one tenth of the mediator's daily rate and therefore depends on the daily fee. The maximum number of hours charged is five and therefore the total charge for this depends on the value of the claim.

LEGAL AID FUNDING OF MEDIATION

2–236 The Legal Aid Board believes that mediation and alternative dispute resolution is desirable, and that it is suitable for medical negligence because it is faster, cheaper and less distressing. Nonetheless, funding is not currently available for mediation.

2–237 The Legal Aid Board has sought approval for funding in a mediation pilot scheme in central London and an NHS pilot scheme. The Lord Chancellor and the Labour Government have both endorsed mediation, but the Legal Aid Board is only prepared to give financial support if the pilot study shows that mediation is being used, and that it is an effective way of resolving disputes about medical cases.

ADVANTAGES OF MEDIATION

1. Speed

2–238 Medical negligence litigation, on average, takes three years before issue of proceedings, four months to serve proceedings and then 18 months to two years before there is a trial. Solicitors and practitioners are sometimes criticised for making use of this full period, but it is often necessary in order to ensure full and thorough investigation and preparation of a case that is likely to be fully defended, although it does mean it is slow. Mediation can provide a more speedy resolution to the problem.

2–239 Mediation seems to allow parties to have an earlier mutual evaluation of their claim. Even if the mediation fails to deliver a settlement or resolution it may still be helpful if the matter goes to trial because, arguably, the parties then have a more focused view of the issues between them.

2. Confidentiality

2–240 Mediation allows parties to air their grievances and discuss areas of concern in a private meeting rather than in the open forum of a court, where there is a public gallery and where many cases are reported by journalists in the national press.

3. Control

The complainants are said to feel that *they* are in control of the **2–241** proceedings rather than the lawyers and the court, and they do not have someone else's view imposed on them. As a result, neither party should feel they have lost. It may also be less confrontational. Much will depend on the parties, of course.

4. Flexibility

It is certainly true that remedies available in mediation are more **2–242** varied because there is greater flexibility than there is in the court process. A mediation is intended to open up a range of possibilities because unlike litigation, mediation can result in more tailored settlements, not just monetary compensation. Examples of imaginative solutions reached so far are:

- A Trust's agreement to incorporate details and suggestions from the complainant's "witness statement" in their new teaching programme so that junior doctors would learn from them. An assurance that the wife of a now deceased complainant should be given her old job back after her husband's death. (She had worked for the health authority being sued and wanted time off to tend her dying husband. The Trust agreed to allow her the time after the claim was mediated.)

- A simple explanation and apology from the doctor involved.

6. Cost

Approximately £200 million is paid out each year by NHS Trusts **2–243** in medical negligence claims. A significant proportion of the expenditure relates to legal costs, *i.e.* rather than compensation to the injured patient. Sometimes the costs equal or surpass the value of the claim.

The Legal Aid Board also spends many millions of pounds a **2–244** year on medical negligence claims. Mediation costs less because it is quicker and less formal without the need for exchange of full evidence.

7. Less stressful

It is well-documented that medical negligence litigation causes **2–245** great stress on clinicians and patients alike. Mediation can help to avoid this by settling complaints as early as possible.

Mediation may be cathartic for both parties. It is very good **2–246** for the plaintiff to have a say in a forum where he or she will be listened to. It can be empowering. A great deal of mediated cases so far have involved the emotional side of the complaint and have been much less to do with monetary compensation.

8. Results

2–247 It has been said that 80 per cent of mediations settle.

DISADVANTAGES OF MEDIATION

1. Sub-optimal outcome

2–248 It is possible that a less advantageous settlement will be achieved for the victim of a medical accident.

2. Practice will not change

2–249 The escalation of litigation has seen a corresponding increase in risk prevention in hospitals, protocols or guidance on good practice, and greater awareness of patients' needs in terms of communication.

2–250 It is unclear whether unreported mediated cases behind closed doors will effect the same pressure as involvement in litigation on NHS management and budgetary systems. The impetus for the prevention of medical accidents and patient focused care may not therefore continue.

3. Lower damages

2–251 It is likely that mediation will result in lower damages in some cases simply because it is often the immediate threat of the court room that pushes defendants into offering realistic damages.

4. Uncensored wrongdoing

2–252 One of the aspects of the litigation process is that it can result in the punishment by his/her own profession of a practitioner guilty of real wrongdoing, or detection of a doctor simply not up to the job. If mediation becomes the norm, what safeguards are there to ensure that the wrongdoing of a practitioner will be punished or that there will be some censure for poor care? Perhaps one should rely on the Trust as employer, but that's what everyone did before the "plethora of litigation". Was it really better for patients? For standards? For society?

5. Insufficient data

2–253 At the moment it is very difficult to assess the advantages and disadvantages of mediation of medical accidents because there have been very few mediated claims.

CONCLUSION

Mediation can seemingly provide certain benefits for the victims **2–254** of medical accidents in appropriate circumstances. However, as relatively few cases have actually been through the mediation process it is impossible to say for certain just how useful it will be as a means of resolving this type of dispute.

A greater understanding of the process by all sides involved **2–255** might be a way of encouraging mediation for suitable cases. If it has benefits for accident victims then surely it is worth serious consideration by all practitioners and advisors working in the field.

FORM ON WHICH PATIENTS MAKE A FORMAL COMPLAINT

TO HELP YOU MAKE A COMPLAINT ABOUT A DOCTOR TO THE GENERAL MEDICAL COUNCIL

You do not have to use this form to make a complaint, but we hope it will help you in making your complaint, and it will help us to consider your complaint as quickly as possible.

PERSONAL DETAILS FOR REFERENCE

1. Your name:

2. Your address and postcode:

3. Daytime telephone number:

4. Home telephone number
   (if different from above)

5. Any fax number to which we could
   send you letters if necessary

6. Are you the patient in the complaint?   YES   NO
   (please tick as appropriate)
   If YES, go to question 9.

7. Are you complaining on someone
   else's behalf?   YES   NO
   (please tick as appropriate)

8. If so, what is your relationship to
   the patient?

DETAILS OF THE DOCTORS

9. The full name of each doctor you are complaining about

A

B

C

10. The address at which each doctor works, if you know it, or the address where you (or the patient) saw each doctor

Dr A.
_____

Dr B
_____

Dr C.
_____

DETAILS OF YOUR COMPLAINT

11. What is your complaint? Please describe your complaint and, if possible include:

- exactly what happened
- the dates on which it happened (as accurately as you can)

(Please use additional pages if you wish)

Note: we will not show your complaint to the doctor without your agreement. But we will need to ask you for consent to do this. If you are prepared to agree that now please tick here _____ .

12. Do you have any documents (for example, letters, medical records) which might back up your complaint? If you do, please send us copies and list them below. (We will return all original documents after taking copies, if you ask us to.)

1.
_____

2.
_____

3.
_____

13. Are there any other people who saw or heard the things you are complaining about? If so, please give their names below, and how they were involved with events.

14. Would those people be prepared to make written statements to the GMC, if necessary?
    (please tick as applicable)

YES   NO

15. We try to resolve most complaints through correspondence but, if it becomes necessary, would you be prepared to be a witness at a public inquiry into your complaint?
    (please tick as applicable)

YES   NO

ANY OTHER COMPLAINT

16. Have you complained to any other organisation about this matter (for example, an NHS health authority, an NHS Trust, the general practice where the doctor works?)
    (please tick as applicable)

YES   NO

If NO, go to question 18.

17. If yes, please say which organisation you have complained to, say briefly what happened to your complaint and send copies of any letters between you and that organisation.

WHERE TO FIND HELP

18. Your Community Health Council or Citizen's Advice Bureau may also be able to help you (their telephone numbers are in the phone book).

19. When you have completed the form, please send it by post to:

Fitness to Practise Directorate
General Medical Council
178 Great Portland Street
London W1N 6JE

or fax it to us on

0171 915 3642

20. Thank you. We will aim to acknowledge receipt of your complaint within one working day of receipt. We aim to send you a reply, or progress report, within four weeks of receiving your complaint. Here is a quick checklist before you post this to us (overleaf).

Have you

- Given us the full name(s) of the doctor(s) concerned?

- Said what your complaint is?

- Said when it happened?

- Sent us any letters about your complaint exchanged between you and any other organisation you have complained to, and other supporting evidence such as medical records?

- Given us your name and, if possible, a daytime telephone number?

CHAPTER 3

NURSES, MIDWIVES and HEALTH VISITORS
—THE UNITED KINGDOM CENTRAL COUNCIL

INTRODUCTION

The United Kingdom Central Council for Nursing, Midwifery **3–01** and Health Visiting ("UKCC", referred to as "the Council") is a statutory body with 60 members, 40 of whom are elected from the profession and 20 appointed by the Secretary of State for Health. The Council's responsibilities are threefold:

1. TO SET STANDARDS FOR AND MAINTAIN A REGISTER OF NURSES, MIDWIVES AND HEALTH VISITORS

The right to practise is conferred by the Council by registration; **3–02** this right may also be removed by the Council.

2. TO ADVISE ON STANDARDS OF PROFESSIONAL CONDUCT

3–03

3. TO DETERMINE CIRCUMSTANCES IN WHICH A PRACTITIONER'S NAME MAY BE REMOVED FROM THE REGISTER

Thus effectively preventing that person continuing to practise. **3–04**

As can be seen, the Council has wide powers in relation to entry and exit from practice, as well as responsibility for training and education and performance in terms of professional conduct. The role which will be dealt with here is that exercised by the Council in respect of complaints about professional misconduct.

PURPOSE OF COMPLAINTS PROCEDURE

3–05 The purpose of the complaints procedure is not to punish the practitioner. Rather, it is to investigate allegations of professional misconduct, and to protect the public from a practitioner who may represent a danger.

3–06 Before making a complaint, therefore, a potential complainant must consider whether the procedure is actually going to provide the outcome he/she is looking for.

3–07 The reality is that it is only worth embarking on a complaint to the UKCC if the desired outcome is the suspension or removal of the practitioner's name from the register for the protection of the public.

3–08 It is important for a potential complainant to appreciate that there are limited sanctions available to the committees dealing with allegations of misconduct and they are (i) temporary or permanent removal of the practitioner's name from the register; or (ii) a caution being entered against the practitioner's name on the register.

PROFESSIONAL MISCONDUCT

3–09 One of the most important functions of the UKCC is to consider allegations of professional misconduct against a registered nurse, midwife or health visitor.

3–10 The two professional conduct committees of the Council investigate complaints about professional conduct. The term misconduct is defined as "conduct unworthy of a registered nurse, midwife or health visitor".[1]

3–11 A code of conduct sets out what is expected of a nurse, midwife or health visitor and this is the yardstick by which someone is judged if called to account for themselves before the professional conduct committees.

Examples of misconduct suitable for referral to the Council include:

- Physical/verbal abuse of patients

- Stealing from patients

[1] The Nurses, Midwives and Health Visitors (Professional Conduct) Rules 1993 Approval Order 1993 (S.I. 1993 No. 893), r.1(2)(k).

- Failing to care for patients properly

- Failing to keep proper records

- Committing a serious criminal offence

- Breach of confidentiality

This is not an exhaustive list.

WHO CAN MAKE A COMPLAINT

Anyone can make a complaint but in the main these are **3–12** received from:
- The police following convictions in criminal courts

- Health authorities/Trusts

- Patients/relatives

- Professional colleagues

HOW TO MAKE A COMPLAINT

A complaint should be made in writing with supporting docu- **3–13** mentation to the Registrar—see Appendix A. The sort of documentation/information which should be included is as follows:

1. An account of the incident;

2. The practitioner's full name, PIN number if known, and address (if known);

3. Description of the practitioner's job at the time of the alleged misconduct;

4. Description of the location, place and time of the incident;

5. If possible, the number of staff on duty and their grades, and the person in charge;

6. Witness statements, for example from other staff, friends or relatives;

7. Copies of any relevant notes, for example accident forms or correspondence with the health care provider, *e.g.* hospital; and

8. Details of any police involvement, for example the name and address of the officer in charge.

BURDEN OF PROOF

3–14 The conduct committees have to decide:

(i) Whether the facts alleged against a practitioner are proven beyond reasonable doubt.

(ii) Whether the alleged incident actually constitutes "professional misconduct".

3–15 The committees apply the criminal standard of proof, *i.e.* beyond reasonable doubt. This is in marked contrast to many disciplinary tribunals where allegations may only be proven on the balance of probabilities or it is more likely than not, or the individual is probably guilty of the alleged conduct.

3–16 It is unlikely that a claim will be sent for consideration by either of the two committees if there is insufficient evidence to establish the case beyond reasonable doubt.

3–17 It may seem a very onerous burden to discharge, but the sanction for those found guilty can be draconian, especially if the practitioner has his/her name removed from the register, thus preventing them from working.

3–18 From the above, therefore, it can be seen that only serious allegations of misconduct which can be proven beyond reasonable doubt should be referred to the UKCC.

3–19 Members of the two committees dealing with allegations of misconduct have two tasks to undertake before making any judgments, suggestions or referrals about a practitioner's registration status, namely (i) and (ii) above.

TIME LIMIT

3–20 There is no time limit, although the complainant may face practical evidential problems if a complaint is not made for a long time after an incident.

COMMITTEE STRUCTURE FOR DEALING WITH COMPLAINTS

The UKCC has three committees which deal with allegations of **3–21** professional misconduct.

1. Preliminary Proceedings Committee
2. Professional Conduct Committee
3. Health Committee

PRELIMINARY PROCEEDINGS COMMITTEE

A complaint is initially considered by the Preliminary Proceed- **3–22** ings Committee ("PPC"). This is a vetting process, by which all claims are assessed to see whether they have merit and are likely to satisfy the burden of proof.

This early screening process also highlights cases where **3–23** immediate action, for example a suspension order (usually an interim suspension order), is required for practitioners who are a danger to patients.

The PPC must consider two factors in deciding what action **3–24** should be taken following a complaint:

1. Can the case be proven beyond reasonable doubt?

2. Is the complaint serious enough to lead to the removal of a practitioner's name from the register in order to protect the public?

The PPC adjudicates on the basis of documentary evidence, **3–25** for example statements and reports, letters, etc. There is no formal hearing. The PPC meets in private. Normally a majority of the 13 members of the Council sit on this particular committee.

The adjudication is not a public hearing and neither the **3–26** practitioner nor the complainant will be present unless the PPC is considering an interim suspension order, in which case the practitioner has the right to attend to make representations to the PPC.

If an interim suspension order is being considered a hearing is **3–27** always set up to consider the case whether the practitioner is present or not.

POWERS OF THE PRELIMINARY PROCEEDINGS COMMITTEE

3–28 Faced with a complaint about serious professional misconduct, the PPC can take one of the following courses of action:

(a) REJECT THE COMPLAINT

3–29 This is usually either because of insufficient evidence to substantiate the case or because the case is not serious enough to lead to removal, *e.g.* a minor road traffic offence. This is quite simply when the PPC decide that the evidence supplied does not satisfy the burden of proof and/or that it is not necessary or appropriate to remove the practitioner's name from the register in order to protect the public. The case is then closed.

(b) ACCEPT THE COMPLAINT

3–30 If the committee accept there may be grounds for complaint the matter is referred to the PPC.

(c) CAUTION ENTERED ON THE REGISTER

3–31 The complaint may be proven but the practitioner's name will not be removed from the UKCC register. Instead the PPC will recommend that a caution be registered against the practitioner's name on the register.

3–32 It should be pointed out that a caution is only considered an option at the PPC stage if, in response to the issue of the notice of proceedings, a practitioner admits the facts and that those facts constitute misconduct. If the committee thinks that there is sufficient mitigation which convinces them that the practitioner is not a danger to the public, then a caution can be given.

3–33 A caution is registered for *five years* and will be reported to any future employers who contact the UKCC to check the prospective employee's registration.

3–34 Although the UKCC literature on complaints procedures states that a caution is not a lesser sanction for a minor offence, but will only be ordered if the conduct might lead to removal from the Registers but the mitigating circumstances suggest that the practitioner is no longer a danger to the public.

3–35 The case is then closed.

An interim suspension is reviewed by the PPC every three months until final consideration by the PCC. Any employer checking a practitioner's registration will be advised of the caution. In addition, the UKCC now routinely circulates to employers lists of those who have received cautions in the same way as details are given of removals and restorations.

(d) INTERIM SUSPENSION

This occurs when a complaint is pending further investigation by **3–36** the PPC or referral to the PCC, and he or she practitioner is regarded as representing an immediate danger to the public.

In these cases an interim suspension is ordered. This is in very **3–37** rare circumstances where the PPC consider the case warrants further investigation, but in order to protect the public in the meantime, and in the practitioner's own interest, the practitioner is suspended from practice pending the outcome of the investigation or a hearing by the PCC.

(e) REFERRAL TO PANEL OF PROFESSIONAL SCREENERS AND HEALTH COMMITTEE

In cases where the practitioner may not be guilty of professional **3–38** misconduct, but his or her actions are likely to be due to ill-health, the PPC would refer the matter to the professional screeners for consideration by the Health Committee.

PROFESSIONAL CONDUCT COMMITTEE

The role of the Professional Conduct Committee ("PCC") is to **3–39** consider cases of alleged misconduct which have been referred to it by the PPC. The PCC has two functions:

1. To consider cases of alleged misconduct which have been referred to it by the PPC.

2. To consider applications for restoration to the register from practitioners previously removed.

PROCEDURE

1. The PCC adjudicates at an open formal hearing.   **3–40**

2. The PCC normally sits with five members of whom one is a representative of a consumer organisation.

3. There are a further two people present at the hearing—a legal assessor to advise on the admissibility of evidence and

points of law, and a Council officer to advise on the Council's procedures.

4. The practitioner can be present and may be legally represented. *N.B.* Legal aid is not available for this representation and so the practitioner must pay privately, or try to get union backing.

5. The complainant may be present and may be legally represented. *N.B.* Legal aid is not available for this representation.

6. The standard of evidence and proof required are that of a criminal court, *i.e.* hearsay evidence is not permissible and the onus of the burden of proof is on the complainant to show beyond reasonable doubt that serious professional misconduct has taken place.

POWERS

(a) Removal from the Register

3–41 It might be helpful to summarise the types of offence which would result, and have resulted in removal from the register and those that do not. The following incidents will result in removal from the register:

(i) reckless and wilful unskilled practice;

(ii) falsifying records;

(iii) concealing untoward events;

(iv) verbal abuse of patients;

(v) theft of patients' belongings;

(vi) breach of confidentiality.

3–42 Incidents which may not result in removal from the register are as follows:

(i) a one-off incident uncharacteristic of the practitioner involved;

(ii) an incident reported by the practitioner straight away, there being no attempt to cover up what happened;

(iii) the incident which was an error of judgment rather than a culpable act.

In cases where an interim suspension is in place, if the facts are **3–43** proven and the misconduct is serious enough to justify removal from the Register, the name will be removed after the PCC hearing.

(b) Rejection of Complaint
This will happen when the burden of proof is not satisfied or it **3–44** would not be appropriate or necessary to remove the practitioner's name from the register or issue a caution if the PPC have not already done so.

THE HEALTH COMMITTEE
This committee looks at whether a practitioner is suffering from **3–45** ill-health which renders him/her unfit to practise.

SOURCES OF REFERRAL
- Preliminary Proceedings Committee   **3–46**
- Professional Conduct Committee
- Health authority/Trust
- Patient's relatives
- Professional colleague

It is important to mention that if at any stage either the PPC or **3–47** the PCC feels there is enough evidence of ill health a person can be referred to the Health Committee.

There are two committees involved with consideration of the **3–48** practitioner's unfitness to practice due to ill-health. They are the Panel of Professional Screeners ("PPS") and the Health Committee. The PPS does just what the title would suggest, namely screen cases before deciding whether they should be referred to the Health Committee.

PROCEDURE
1. The referral from the PPC or a complaint from outside the **3–49** UKCC plus supporting documentation are sent to the PPS.

2. The Council solicitor draws up a statutory declaration for **3–50** the person making the allegation of ill health to sign. This

could be the employer or any individual concerned about a practitioner's fitness to practise. This document is legally required before an investigation can go ahead.

3–51 3. Once the statutory declaration is signed and returned to the Council by the practitioner, the investigation commences.

3–52 4. All of the documentation is initially scrutinised by the PPS, which decides whether the case is going to be reviewed or not. If the case is not going to be reviewed, the case is closed.

3–53 5. If the case proceeds then the panel refers the case to one of a specialist panel of medical examiners for an independent report.

3–54 6. Once the report is received it is then submitted to the PPS. Again, if no case is proven then the file is closed.

3–55 7. If the medical report is positive then the matter is referred to the Health Committee, the PPC or the PCC.

3–56 8. The Health Committee meets in private and comprises five members plus a legal assessor to advise on the admissibility of evidence and points of law, and one Council officer to advise on Council procedures, plus the medical expert who has provided a report.

3–57 9. The practitioner is encouraged to attend and can be legally represented, but again legal aid is not available and so the practitioner must pay privately for the legal representation or seek union assistance.

3–58 10. The standard of evidence is that of a criminal court, but the standard of proof is on the balance of probabilities. *i.e.* it is more likely than not that the practitioner is suffering from ill health. Contrast this to the standard of proof from the PPC to PCC.

APPEALS

3–59 Section 12 of the Nurses, Midwives and Health Visitors' Act 1997 gives a person a right of appeal to the High Court as follows:

"(1) A person aggrieved by a decision to remove him from the register or to direct that his registration in the register be suspended or to remove or alter any entry in respect of him, or by any decision under section 10(3) or (4), may, *within three months* after the date on which notice of the decision was given to him by the Council, appeal to the appropriate court, and on the appeal—

    (a) The court may give such directions in the matter as it thinks proper, including directions as to the cost of the appeal; and

    (b) The order of the court should be final.

(2) The appropriate court for the purposes of this section is the High Court, the Court of Session or the High Court in Northern Ireland, according as the appellant's ordinary place of residence is in England and Wales, Scotland or Northern Ireland at the time when notice of the decision was given." (Emphasis added.]

It is not clear whether or not the complainant is entitled to **3–60** know that the practitioner wishes to appeal, or that an appeal has taken place and so any complainant wishing to know should check with the UKCC after adjudication of the complaint to see whether or not the practitioner is amounting an appeal. The complainant cannot become involved with the appeals process.

CONCLUSION

The UKCC publishes a very good information booklet regarding **3–61** the complaints procedure for registered nurses. It is well written and easy to understand. There is sufficient detail to enable anyone wishing to make a complaint to do so. Anyone wishing to obtain a copy of the UKCC booklet on complaints about professional conduct should write to the Director of Professional Conduct at the UKCC. The address is to be found in Appendix A.

It should be noted, however, that the purpose of the procedure is not to punish the practitioner nor to compensate the complainant. Also, the complainant is not party to the process. Once the complaint is received the UKCC itself picks up the complaint to start proceedings.

A SIMPLIFIED ILLUSTRATION OF THE PROCESS BY WHICH AN ALLEGATION OF MISCONDUCT IS CONSIDERED BY THE PRELIMINARY PROCEEDINGS COMMITTEE

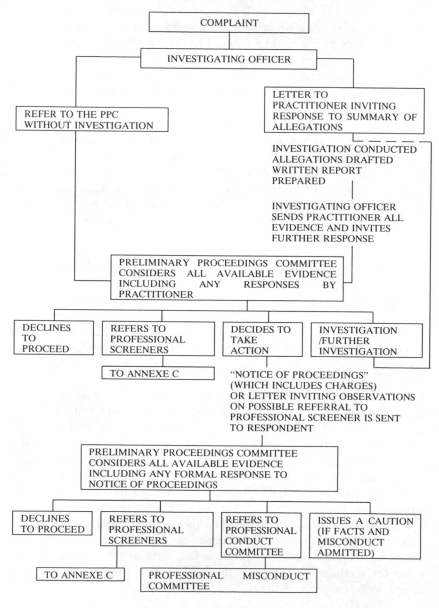

A SIMPLIFIED ILLUSTRATION OF THE PROCESS BY WHICH AN ALLEGATION OF MISCONDUCT IS CONSIDERED BY THE PROFESSIONAL CONDUCT COMMITTEE

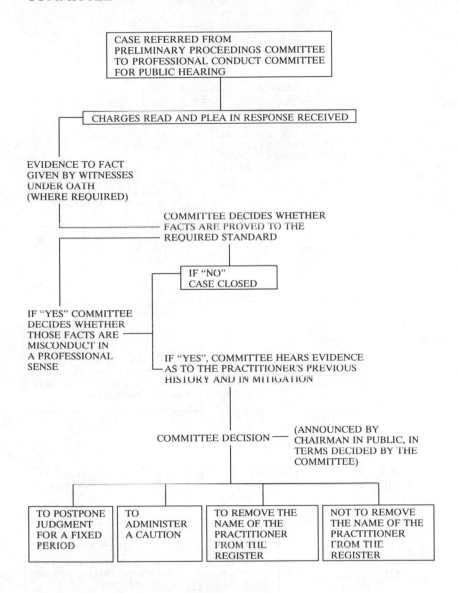

A SIMPLIFIED ILLUSTRATION OF THE PROCESS BY WHICH COMPLAINTS ALLEGING UNFITNESS TO PRACTISE ARE CONSIDERED

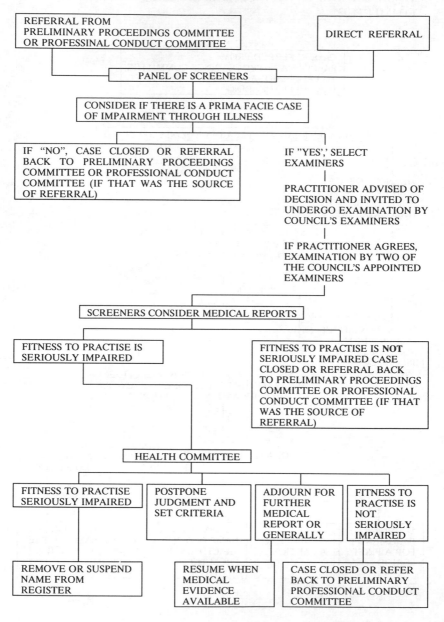

REFERRAL FROM PRELIMINARY PROCEEDINGS COMMITTEE OR PROFESSINAL CONDUCT COMMITTEE

DIRECT REFERRAL

PANEL OF SCREENERS

CONSIDER IF THERE IS A PRIMA FACIE CASE OF IMPAIRMENT THROUGH ILLNESS

IF "NO", CASE CLOSED OR REFERRAL BACK TO PRELIMINARY PROCEEDINGS COMMITTEE OR PROFESSIONAL CONDUCT COMMITTEE (IF THAT WAS THE SOURCE OF REFERRAL)

IF "YES',' SELECT EXAMINERS

PRACTITIONER ADVISED OF DECISION AND INVITED TO UNDERGO EXAMINATION BY COUNCIL'S EXAMINERS

IF PRACTITIONER AGREES, EXAMINATION BY TWO OF THE COUNCIL'S APPOINTED EXAMINERS

SCREENERS CONSIDER MEDICAL REPORTS

FITNESS TO PRACTISE IS SERIOUSLY IMPAIRED

FITNESS TO PRACTISE IS **NOT** SERIOUSLY IMPAIRED CASE CLOSED OR REFERRAL BACK TO PRELIMINARY PROCEEDINGS COMMITTEE OR PROFESSIONAL CONDUCT COMMITTEE (IF THAT WAS THE SOURCE OF REFERRAL)

HEALTH COMMITTEE

FITNESS TO PRACTISE SERIOUSLY IMPAIRED

POSTPONE JUDGMENT AND SET CRITERIA

ADJOURN FOR FURTHER MEDICAL REPORT OR GENERALLY

FITNESS TO PRACTISE IS NOT SERIOUSLY IMPAIRED

REMOVE OR SUSPEND NAME FROM REGISTER

RESUME WHEN MEDICAL EVIDENCE AVAILABLE

CASE CLOSED OR REFER BACK TO PRELIMINARY PROFESSIONAL CONDUCT COMMITTEE

CHAPTER 4

DENTISTS—GENERAL DENTAL COUNCIL

INTRODUCTION

The General Dental Council is a statutory body which was **4–01** established in order to regulate the dental profession. The relevant statute is the Dentists Act 1984. It comprises 50 individuals, of whom six are non-dentists. The main three functions of the Council, which will be covered in this text, are as follows:

1. Maintaining a register of dentists **4–02**

The right to practice is conferred by the Council by registration and this right may also be removed by the Council.

2. Regulating the professional conduct of dentists and their fitness to practise.

3. Establishing and maintaining high standards of dental education both before and after qualification.

The first two functions are the ones that will be dealt with in this text.

The situation is very clear in respect of registration—it is an **4–03** offence against the Dentists Act 1984 for an unregistered person to engage in practice of dentistry. It is the responsibility of all dentists who intend to practise to renew their registration annually, and failure to do so may lead to disciplinary proceedings.

In addition, under section 27 of the Dentists Act 1984, the **4–04** Council has the right to remove dentists' names from the register for conduct amounting to serious professional misconduct.

4–05   The Council has published a booklet entitled *Professional Conduct and Fitness to Practise* which is available from the Registrar at the address given in Appendix A.

PURPOSE OF COMPLAINTS PROCEDURE

4–06 The Council's jurisdiction is restricted to considering matters of serious professional misconduct or of serious impairment to health. The Council does not operate a complaints procedure as such. *N.B.* Those wishing to make complaints about a dentist's treatment may be better advised pursuing the matter via the local resolution stage and then, if not satisfied, using the NHS complaints procedures.

SERIOUS PROFESSIONAL MISCONDUCT

4–07 There is no definition of serious professional misconduct in the Council's own guides to professional conduct, but examples of the type of action which may fall within the category are provided, and would suggest that serious professional misconduct is any conduct which is likely to bring the dental profession into disrepute.

4–08   Examples of serious professional misconduct are as follows:

- Non-compliance with Council guidelines on anaesthesia and sedation.

- Failing to take proper precautions to prevent cross infection, *e.g.* HIV.

- Failing to seek medical advice and supervision in the event that the dentist him or herself has an infection which can be transmitted to patients, *e.g.* HIV.

- Unsafe disposal of clinical, hazardous waste.

- Lack of consent to treatment by the patient because the dentist did not properly explain a procedure and the risks.

- Dishonesty, violence, indecency or breach of confidentiality.

- Criminal convictions such as fraud, theft, unlawful possession of controlled drugs or acts of indecency.

- Failing to have set up a practice-based system for dealing with patients' complaints after 1996.

The list is not exhaustive, but in addition to advising as to **4–09** what may constitute serious professional misconduct, the Council also provides helpful guidelines for dentists on their level of responsibility and what constitutes proper and acceptable practice.

It should perhaps be noted that the sort of complaints to **4–10** constitute serious professional misconduct are probably not the most common complaints that patients would make. For example, there is no reference to over-treatment, *i.e.* treatment that cannot be physically justified, nor the standard of treatment. Arguably, these would be covered under the description of "conduct likely to bring the dental profession into disrepute", but arguably they do not fall within that category.

WHO CAN MAKE A COMPLAINT

Anyone can make a complaint to the General Dental Council. **4–11** Complaints may be received from the following:

- The police, following convictions in criminal courts

- Reports from tribunals or health service committees

- Patients and relatives

- Professional colleagues

- Community health councils

N.B. If there has been serious professional misconduct, any- **4–12** one making a complaint must be acting in a public capacity, *e.g.* officer of a health authority, policeman, or if not then additional documentation may need to be provided, for example if it is a private individual wishing to make a complaint—see the section on Procedure at paragraphs 22—4–23 below.

There are now two stages to the procedure. One is by way of **4–13** local resolution of a complaint, *i.e.* at the practice itself. The second is by way of committees set up by the council.

PROCEDURE

STAGE 1—LOCAL RESOLUTION—COMPLAINTS TO THE PRACTICE

4–14 Prior to April 1, 1996, patients wishing to complain about dental treatment did so by contacting their local family health service authority. The only way of succeeding to show that a dentist had actually done something wrong was to establish that he/she was in breach of terms of service, *i.e.* his or her contractual obligation with the health authority. A complex procedure existed whereby each side submitted evidence and then there was a hearing, and some time later the complainant was informed of the outcome.

4–15 This system was swept away by the changes to the NHS complaints procedures which came into effect on April 1, 1996.

4–16 A new sub-paragraph to the guide on *Professional Conduct and Fitness to Practise* concerning complaints made to dental practices was written and approved by the Council in May 1996. It provides:

"*34* . . . *(viii)*. Complaints—if a patient should have cause to complain about the service provided at a dental practice, it is in the interests of both the patient and dentist for the matter to be resolved at practice level. The complaint may relate to the treatment provided or some other matter, such as the payment of fees or the attitude of staff. Dentists are advised to establish a practice based procedure for resolving patients' complaints. The Council would endorse the detailed guidance on handling complaints which has been issued by the NHS Executive in their Guidance for General Dental Practitioners, *Complaints—Listening . . . Acting . . . Improving.* Information on handling complaints is also available from the British Dental Association. The Council would regard a failure to establish a practice-based complaints procedure as likely to raise a question of serious professional misconduct."

STAGE II—INVESTIGATION BY THE COUNCIL

4–17 A complaint should be made direct to the practice. This can be done orally or in writing, but should include the following:

- Name and address of dentist.

- Place and time of incident.

- Details of the circumstances giving rise to complaint.

- Complainant's name and address.

Where the complainant does not receive a satisfactory response **4–18** from the practice, they can go on to complain to the Dental Practice Council. It is also open to the complainant to take the matter further by way of the health authority, by writing to the complaints manager at the health authority whereupon the complaint will be dealt with in accordance with the procedure outlined in Chapter 1.

Alternatively, the complainant may wish to take the matter to **4–19** the Health Service Ombudsman, who is now empowered to look at clinical aspects of health care.

If a complainant is not satisfied with the answer he/she has **4–20** received from the practice, the procedure for local resolution fails, or the complaint is too serious to be dealt with at a local level and should actually be dealt with straight away by the General Dental Council, and the complainant does not wish to pursue an NHS complaints procedure, the complaint should be referred to the General Dental Council.

It is important to remember that the Council deals with **4–21** serious professional misconduct and not clinical error or substandard care.

COMPLAINTS TO THE GENERAL DENTAL COUNCIL

If local resolution is not possible then the complainant should **4–22** write to the Registrar of the General Dental Council. The complainant should include the following details/documentation:

- A letter or statement setting out the facts and what the complaint is about.

- Affidavit/statutory declaration about the alleged serious professional misconduct, including dates, if possible, and what treatment was carried out. This statement should include:

(1) Name, address and occupation of the complainant and practitioner.
(2) Details of incident, *e.g.* date, time, place, facts.
(3) Why complaint is being made, *i.e.* grounds for complaint.

- Any supporting documentation, *e.g.* appointment cards, copies of any invoices or receipts for relevant treatment.

- Witness statements or hospital reports, *e.g.* if the patient was then taken to hospital.

Time Limit

4–23 There is no time limit on complaints to the General Dental Council, but there are obviously practical evidential difficulties if the complaint is not reported within a reasonable period of time after the incident—not least that a full and thorough investigation may no longer be possible, if staff at the practice have moved on and memories faded.

STRUCTURE

4–24 There are three committees which deal with allegations of professional misconduct.

1. Preliminary Proceedings Committee

2. Professional Conduct Committee

3. Health Committee

PRELIMINARY PROCEEDINGS COMMITTEE

COMPOSITION

4–25 Five Council members plus the President. At least one member of the committee must be a non-dentist.

PROCEDURE

4–26 1. Once a complaint is received by the Registrar for the Council, it is initially considered by the Preliminary Proceedings Committee. This is a vetting process, by which all claims are assessed to see whether they have merit and fall within the ambit of professional misconduct, and whether the complainant is likely to succeed in establishing professional misconduct and/or that the dentist is not fit to practice.

2. The Committee sits in private.

3. There are usually two meetings of the Committee each year in March and September, but the Committee can sit more often if the need arises.

4. The Committee reviews the evidence submitted to the Registrar and assesses whether the case should be referred to the Professional Conduct Committee or the Health Committee.

POSSIBLE OUTCOMES

(a) Rejection of Complaint
This is usually due to insufficient evidence, but it can be because 4–27 there are not reasonable grounds for the complainant proceeding with the complaint.

(b) Warning to the Practitioner
This happens when there is insufficient evidence to warrant 4–28 referral to the Professional Conduct Committee, but the dentist should be warned that the Preliminary Proceedings Committee might reconsider its decision if further evidence or further complaints come to light.

(c) Interim Suspension
This occurs when there is sufficient evidence of misconduct to 4–29 warrant referral to the Professional Conduct Committee, and the Preliminary Proceedings Committee takes the view that the dentist may be an immediate danger to the public and that it would not be safe to allow him or her to continue to practise until the Professional Conduct Committee has had the opportunity to consider the case.

It should be noted that the Preliminary Proceedings Com- 4–30 mittee can only make an interim suspension order if the dentist has been informed of the possibility and given the opportunity to make representations, either in person or through an adviser, *e.g.* a solicitor.

4–31   Once made, a dentist can apply to the High Court for the termination of the order, presumably if he/she feels that it is not justified in the first instance or the grounds no longer exist.

(d) Referral to a Professional Conduct Committee

4–32 This occurs when there is sufficient evidence of misconduct to warrant referral to the Professional Conduct Committee.

PROFESSIONAL CONDUCT COMMITTEE

COMPOSITION

4–33 10 members of Council plus the President. At least two members of the committee must be non-dentists.

ROLE

4–34 The role of the Professional Conduct Committee ("PCC") is to consider cases of alleged misconduct which have been referred to it by the Preliminary Proceedings Committee ("PPC"). Unlike the Preliminary Proceedings Committee, the Professional Conduct Committee does not simply rely on the paperwork. Instead, arrangements are made for a formal hearing of the complaint against the practitioner.

PROCEDURE

4–35   1. The hearing is held in public.

2. A notice of inquiry with a notice of hearing is sent to the dentist at least *four weeks* before the hearing.

3. The Committee normally sits twice a year in May and November, but can meet at any time should the need arise. Presumably the reason why the meetings are a couple of months after the PPC meetings is to ensure that matters referred by the PPC can be dealt with promptly by the PCC a couple of months later.

4. The Committee is assisted by a lawyer who will be a barrister or a solicitor of at least 10 years' post-qualification experience, who advises on points of law.

5. Evidence is given on oath and rules of evidence are almost the same as in a court of law, in that the prosecution gives evidence first with the opportunity for cross examination

and the defence case is put to the Committee with the opportunity for cross examination.

6. The burden of proof is beyond reasonable doubt as in criminal cases.

7. Although evidence is mainly given verbally, documentary evidence in support, *i.e.* the original complaint and the dentist's response, is considered and also, if relevant, the dental records.

8. Both sides can be legally represented.

9. The Committee then decides whether the burden of proof has been satisfied.

10. The Committee makes its decision and informs the dentist and complainant.

POSSIBLE OUTCOMES

If the PCC finds that the dentist has been guilty of serious **4–36** professional misconduct, the Committee has to go on to consider whether the gravity of one offence (or if there is more than one offence, the cumulative offence) is so serious that the public need to be protected from the dentist. A decision may be immediate or postponed until the next meeting of the Committee.

(a) Case Dismissed
If the dentist is not guilty, the dentist and complainant are **4–37** simply informed and the matter is not taken any further.

(b) Postponed decision
This is so that the Committee can monitor the dentist's conduct **4–38** in the intervening period to see whether there is an improvement in the dentist's behaviour or standards.

(c) Suspension of the Dentist from the Register
This need not be permanent but arises if the dentist's conduct is **4–39** so serious that the Committee think the public should be protected. The decision takes effect within *28 days*, unless the Committee thinks it should take immediate effect.

(d) Erasure of the Dentist's name from the Register

4–40 This is only done if the dentist's conduct is so bad that the public needs to be protected by permanent removal of the dentist's name from the register. This effectively assures that the dentist can no longer practice dentistry because a dentist can only practice if he/she is registered. Again, the decision takes effect within *28 days*, unless the Committee thinks that erasure should take immediate effect.

HEALTH COMMITTEE

4–41 The Dentists Act 1984 gives the General Dental Council jurisdiction in cases where a dentists fitness to practice is "seriously impaired" by reason of physical or mental ill-health.

WHO CAN COMPLAIN

4–42 Any person, or any organisation, with grounds for thinking that this is the case.

HOW TO MAKE A COMPLAINT

4–43 A letter should be written to the General Dental Council setting out the reasons for concern with supporting evidence if appropriate or available.

PROCEDURE

4–44 This is set out in the General Dental Council Health Committee (Procedures) Rules 1984[1] which also set out terms for the operation of the Health Committee.

4–45   1. Information is first considered by the Council President or by another member of the Council duly appointed to carry out this task.

4–46   2. If the President does not agree that there is sufficient evidence of ill-health or fitness to practise, the complaint is not taken any further.

4–47   3. If the President does think that there is evidence that the dentist's fitness to practise may be affected by ill-health, he or she can take one of the following steps:

---

[1] S.I. 1984 No. 2010.

(a) Inform the dentist who has *14 days* to be examined by at least two medical practitioners. The medical practitioners are chosen by the President from panels nominated by professional bodies.

(b) Consider the medical reports on the fitness to practice of the dentist, and, if there is evidence of ill-health, decide how this is best managed or treated.

(c) Consider any report made by the dentist's own medical practitioner before reaching a decision.

4. In certain situations, the President or members of the **4–48** Health Committee may invite the dentist to attend the meeting of the Health Committee. Examples of this are:

- the dentist refuses to be examined by the medical practitioners appointed by the Health Committee
- medical opinion is unanimously agreed that the dentist is unfit to practise
- medical opinion is divided as to whether the dentist is fit to practise
- medical evidence suggests that the dentist is fit to practise but only on limited cases.

In other words, the Health Committee almost always wants to see the dentist.

5. Meetings are in private. **4–49**

6. The main evidence is from the two medical examiners and **4–50** possibly a medical examiner appointed by the dentist.

7. The Committee is assisted by a legal assessor and medical **4–51** assessors.

POSSIBLE OUTCOMES

(a) Adjournment for more evidence
This occurs when the Committee does not feel that there is **4–52** sufficient evidence to come to a decision.

(b) Conditions imposed on registration
This would arise when the Committee do not think that the **4–53** dentist is actually unfit to practise but needs to improve methods of practice or behaviour. Conditions can only be imposed for a maximum of *three years*.

(c) Suspension of the Dentist's name from the Register

4–54 This is if a complaint is actually proven, but the Committee can only suspend the dentist for a maximum of *12 months*.

APPEALS

4–55 A dentist whose name has been erased from the register may apply to the Professional Conduct Committee to have his/her name restored to the register not less than *10 months* after erasure.

4–56 An appeal must be made within *28 days* of the committee decision.

4–57 When considering such an application, the PCC will take the following into account:

(i) The circumstances which led to the erasure in the first place.

(ii) Evidence of the dentist's conduct during the period of erasure, *i.e.* steps he/she has taken to improve professional conduct.

4–58 A dentist can also appeal against a suspension order or erasure by either the PCC or the Health Committee by way of an appeal to the Judicial Committee of the Privy Council. However, if the PCC thinks that it would be in the best interests of the public or the dentist, it can still order suspension or erasure with immediate effect, notwithstanding any appeals to the Privy Council.

4–59 In other words, the dentist will remain suspended or have his/her name erased from the register whilst the appeal is pending, and if it is thought that he/she is a danger to the public.

CONCLUSION

4–60 The General Dental Council has a comprehensive procedure for dealing with serious professional misconduct but it is not empowered to deal with complaints about clinical competence or negligence. For those issues the NHS complaints procedures may be more helpful, either prior to or instead of initiating legal action.

NOTICE OF INQUIRY

[Date]

Sir/Madam   **4–61**

On behalf of the General Dental Council notice is hereby given to you that in consequence of [a complaint made against you to the Council] or [information received by the Council] an inquiry is to be held into the following charge (charges) against you:—

(If the charge relates to conviction) That you were on the   day of [specify month and year] at (specify court recording the conviction) convicted of (set out particulars of the conviction in sufficient detail to identify the case).

or

(If the charge relates to conduct) That being a registered dentist you (set out briefly the facts alleged): and that in relation to the facts alleged you have been guilty of serious professional misconduct.

(Where there is more than one charge, the charges are to be numbered consecutively, charges relating to conviction being set out before charges relating to conduct.)

Notice is further given to you that on [day of the week,] the day of [specify month and year]   , a meeting of the Professional Conduct Committee of the Council will be held at [venue]   , at [time]   , to consider the above-mentioned charge (charges) against you, and to determine whether or not they should direct the Registrar to erase your name from the Register, or suspend your registration therein, pursuant to section 27 of the Act.

You are hereby invited to answer in writing the above-mentioned charge (charges) and also to appear before the Committee at the place and time specified above, for the purpose of answering it (them). You may appear in person or by counsel or solicitor, or by any officer or member of any organisation of which you are a member, or by a professional colleague, or by any member of your family. The Committee have power, if you do not appear, to hear and decide upon the said charge (charges) in your absence.

Any answer, admission, or other statement or communication, which you may desire to make with respect to the said charge (charges), should be addressed to the Solicitor to the Council.

If you desire to make any application that the inquiry should be postponed, you should send the application to the Solicitor to the Council as soon as may be, stating the grounds on which you desire a postponement. Any such application will be considered by the President of the General Dental Council in accordance with the General Dental Council Professional Conduct Committee (Procedure) Rules 1984 (S.I. 1984 No. 1517) a copy of which is sent herewith for your information.

I am, Sir/Madam,
Your obedient Servant,

CHAPTER 5

PHARMACISTS—ROYAL PHARMACEUTICAL SOCIETY OF GREAT BRITAIN

INTRODUCTION

All pharmacists must be registered with the Royal Pharmaceutical Society of Great Britain before they can practise or be employed as a pharmacist. **5–01**

The Royal Pharmaceutical Society has its own disciplinary **5–02** machinery which is similar to that of other professional organisations. It differs in that it also has a statutory duty to enforce various sections of the Medicines Act 1968 and the Poisons Act 1972. In order to fulfil those duties, the Society has a full time inspectorate which carries out both routine monitoring and special investigations.

Pharmacists employed by the NHS are subject to the terms **5–03** and conditions of their employment contract, and in cases involving a breach of duty of care they will be subject to the same legal process and the same burden of proof as their fellow NHS employees such as doctors and nurses.

In the event of an error or substandard care by a pharmacist **5–04** working in the private sector, then obviously a person would have redress in contract law.

As well as seeking redress through the NHS, or in contract law, patients may also wish to make a complaint to the Society.

WHO CAN COMPLAIN

Anyone who has a legitimate complaint about the standard of **5–05** service provided by a pharmacist in the NHS or in private practice.

TYPES OF COMPLAINT

5–06 • Criminal convictions.

• Serious misconduct.

• Allegations of offences under the Medicines Act 1968 or the Poisons Act 1972.

HOW TO MAKE A COMPLAINT

5–07 Interestingly, there are two ways in which complaints may be made to the Society: first, direct to the Disciplinary Committee; and secondly, to the Professional Standards Department at the address given in Appendix A.

5–08 The sort of documentation/information which should be included is as follows:

• An account of the incident, including the place, date and what actually happened.

• The pharmacist's full name, if known.

• Any supporting documentation.

• Witness statements, for example from anyone who either saw what happened at the time of the incident, or afterwards. The latter would apply in the event of a wrongful prescription where a patient had suffered adverse consequences as a result of taking tablets which were incorrectly labelled.

• Details of any criminal conviction.

TIME LIMIT

5–09 None, although the complainant may face practical evidential problems if the complaint is not made for a long time after an incident.

DISCIPLINARY COMMITTEE

As stated, a complaint can first be made directly to the **5–10** Disciplinary Committee. However, the Committee has no inspectors or facility to carry out an investigation, and the complainant would therefore need to be able to furnish all the necessary evidence to lead to a finding of misconduct. Generally speaking, direct referrals are often passed to the Professional Standards Department for investigation in any event. Therefore, a direct referral is not usual and may not be of any benefit.

PROFESSIONAL STANDARDS DEPARTMENT

Complaints to the Professional Standards Department can be in **5–11** relation to alleged professional misconduct or an alleged offence, or a mixture of both.

Inspectors are employed by the Professional Standards **5–12** Department and have a dual function. First, they gather evidence in relation to the complaint and prepare reports.

If the investigation has been requested by the Disciplinary **5–13** Committee (see above) the report will be referred back to the committee. In the vast majority of cases the report will follow an investigation after receipt of a complaint to the Professional Standards Department. Reports are considered by the department and, if sufficiently serious, will be referred to the Society's Council, which might order criminal prosecution or referral to the Disciplinary Committee.

The second function of the inspectors is to help assist any **5–14** pharmacists involved to review their system in order to prevent a repetition of any malpractice or professional misconduct.

POSSIBLE OUTCOMES

Much depends upon who actually investigates the complaint. **5–15**

PROFESSIONAL STANDARDS DEPARTMENT

If it is the Law Department, then the department's inspectors **5–16** will report, and those reports will be considered. Either the Professional Standards Department's enforcement division will take action against the pharmacist by (i) giving advice, (ii) formal warning or (iii) prosecution on direction of the Council, or if the Council decides the matter should be dealt with professionally the matter will be referred to the Disciplinary Committee.

DISCIPLINARY COMMITTEE

5–17 The Disciplinary Committee deals with all relevant criminal convictions as well as serious allegations of misconduct. The Committee has the power to take various steps in the event of the case being proven.

(a) Admonishment or reprimand

(b) Adjournment
This is usually for a period of 12 months so that improvements can be monitored.

(c) Removal from Register
5–18 Removal of a pharmacist's name from the register.

(d) Disqualification of Companies
5–19 Disqualification of companies from operating a pharmacy.

(e) Removal of Pharmacy premises from the Register
5–20 Removal of pharmacy premises from the register, as opposed to an individual pharmacist.

CONCLUSION

5–21 As far as the author is aware, there is no booklet or pamphlet published by the Society giving details of the process by which claims of misconduct are investigated. It is suggested that as a first line of complaint, the Professional Standards Department can be approached and advice sought on whether the investigation of a complaint would fall within their remit or not. The address of the head of the inspectorate and the enforcement division of the Professional Standards Department is given in Appendix A.

However, it should be borne in mind that for any pharmacist **5–22** working within the NHS, the health service complaints procedures will operate. If a pharmacist is working independently in the private sector a would-be complainant may be able to rely on breach of implied terms of contract.

It may be useful to inform the Society of a complaint or legal action against a pharmacist who is a member.

CHAPTER 6

OSTEOPATHS—GENERAL OSTEOPATHIC COUNCIL

INTRODUCTION

At the time of writing, the regulation of osteopaths is in a **6–01** transitional stage between voluntary regulation of the profession and statutory regulation and registration.

The latter is as a result of pressure from within and outside **6–02** the profession resulting in the Osteopaths' Act 1993. This provides the statutory framework for the establishment of a new Council and sets out amongst other things, the Council's functions in terms of registration and regulating the standards of the profession.

Prior to April 1, 1997, there were a number of registering **6–03** bodies for those qualified as osteopaths. Of these the General Council and Register of Osteopaths ("GCRO") was by far the largest registering body. Other organisations included:

(a) The College of Osteopaths Practitioners Association and Register.

(b) The British and European Osteopathic Association.

(c) The Guild of Osteopaths.

(d) The Natural Therapeutic and Osteopathic Society and Register.

(e) The London and Counties Society of Physiologists.

It should be noted that in the past registration was voluntary **6–04** and even the GCRO had little idea as to how many people might be practising as osteopaths.

99

6–05   The GCRO was established in 1936 and was run by a full time professional secretariat, whereas the others stemmed mainly from the 1970s and were, generally speaking, run on a part-time basis by the osteopaths themselves without full-time professional assistance.

6–06   The GCRO published a handbook of professional conduct for registered osteopaths, which contained the procedure for disciplining members guilty of professional misconduct. Since April 1997 this procedure has ceased to operate as the General Osteopathic Council is now responsible for regulating the profession.

6–07   The training itself has changed over the last few years, and a growing proportion is degree-based. The degree course lasts four years, at the end of which time those who have passed both the practical and theoretical aspects are awarded a Bachelor of Science degree.

6–08   The new General Osteopathic Council ("GOSC") regulates the whole of the profession. Registration with the Council is compulsory and only members who have trained on accredited and recognised courses are eligible for registration.

6–09   The new organisation has several functions including:

1. Maintaining a register of osteopaths.

2. Promoting and ensuring a high standard of education and professional competence, and the continuing professional development of those osteopaths on the register. This will be achieved by:
    (i) publishing guidelines on good professional practice; and
    (ii) assessing, monitoring and accrediting education courses.

3. Operating a complaints and disciplinary procedure.

6–10   The GCRO represented approximately 1,600 osteopaths. It is likely that the GOSC will have 3,000 members on the register by the time the registration process is complete. Again it is difficult to be precise because the exact number of osteopaths practising in the United Kingdom is not known.

PROCESS OF REGISTRATION

This can usefully be divided into two headings. **6–11**

INITIAL REGISTRATION
The register was opened in May 1998. Would-be registrants **6–12** have two years in which to register. After that period, it will be an offence for anyone not registered to use the title of osteopath.

A Registrar and team have been appointed, and their func- **6–13** tions include processing applications for registration.

It will not be possible for practitioners currently registered **6–14** with another body simply to transfer registration to the new register.

The Registrar needs to be satisfied that an applicant will **6–15** practise:

(i) lawfully;

(ii) competently; and

(iii) safely.

A system has been devised whereby the practitioner's compe- **6–16** tence can be evaluated from documentation submitted with the application form.

An applicant has to complete an application form which will **6–17** contain general or personal information such as name and address and place of the practice. In addition, each applicant has to fill out what is known as a professional profile and portfolio. This document contains a series of questions designed to test the practical competence of the applicant in 14 different areas. It has been carefully designed to ensure that practitioners are obliged to consider how they operate in practical profes- sional situations.

Moreover, the Registrar reserves the right to visit the appli- **6–18** cant's premises and to request that the applicant performs a practical assessment.

By these methods, the Registrar will be able to ensure that **6–19** the applicant has attained a standard of proficiency in accord- ance with the requirements and terms of the Osteopaths' Act 1993. The process is designed to be fair and transparent.

6–20 Any applicant who is dissatisfied with the Registrar's decision can make representations to the GOSC and ultimately appeal to the Privy Council.

SUBSEQUENT REGISTRATION

6–21 Any applicant qualifying from an accredited institution offering a programme with recognised qualification status ("RQS") will be eligible to apply for registration unless further information as to conduct or competence should come to the Registrar's attention which might affect the application, *e.g.* a criminal conviction. Osteopaths will be required to indicate, on an annual basis, that they wish to remain on the register.

6–22 One of the other functions of the GOSC is to implement a system of accreditation for RQS training courses. This accreditation process takes place at the same time and alongside the first registration.

6–23 The GOSC is required to maintain high standards of professional competence and professional development and education for registered members.

6–24 In addition, indemnity insurance will be required for registered members.

COMPLAINTS SYSTEM

6–25 Full details of the complaints system to be put in place are not yet known. However, the Osteopaths' Act provides for a two-tier system for dealing with complaints, involving an investigation committee and then a Professional Conduct Committee. Precise details as to the workings of these two committees, their composition and functions, are not yet available.

6–26 Obviously, the GOSC will only have jurisdiction to deal with complaints regarding registered members. If complaints arise in relation to the treatment of practitioners who are unregistered, *i.e.* in the next two years, then the patient may not have any means of redress. In the event of a practitioner being registered with one of the former registering bodies then a complaint should be addressed to those organisations.

6–27 It is also worth mentioning that while the process of registration continues, the Registrar may well detect grounds for concern about would-be registered osteopaths, or information may come to light, such as criminal convictions which would mean that notwithstanding the fact that a formal system is not yet fully in place, the Registrar would ask the GOSC to consider some form of investigation into the applicant's professional practice.

CONCLUSION

At the time of writing, the GOSC is implementing the com- **6–28** pulsory registration and regulation of the whole of the osteopathic profession.

This will be achieved by putting in place a system of registra- **6–29** tion, accreditation, continuing professional development and guidelines on good professional practice. *N.B.* In the future, registered osteopaths will have no professional qualifications recorded after their name, because the GOSC takes the view that this can be confusing. A registered practitioner will simply be known as a registered osteopath.

It will be possible to contact the GOSC to check whether a **6–30** practitioner is in fact registered. Anyone not registered should not be practising within two years of the register opening. It would clearly be in any potential patients' interest to ask a practitioner whether or not he/she is registered with the new GOSC, or intends to do so, or has an application currently being processed, before embarking on treatment. If the practitioner will not say, or the patient is too embarrassed to ask, then it is always possible to telephone the GOSC for details. The address and telephone number can be found in Appendix A.

CHAPTER 7

PHYSIOTHERAPISTS—THE CHARTERED SOCIETY OF PHYSIOTHERAPISTS

INTRODUCTION

At the time of writing, anyone can call him/herself a phys- **7–01** iotherapist and practice physiotherapy. However, a chartered or state-registered physiotherapist can be identified by the letters after his/her name as someone who has completed a three to four year degree course at an accredited institution and who has been trained to a high professional standard.

Treatment is provided by a qualified physiotherapist governed **7–02** by a code of professional conduct, and the practitioner is insured in the event of an accident or injury occurring to a patient during the treatment. There are two bodies concerned with the professional conduct of state-registered and/or chartered physiotherapists.

CHARTERED SOCIETY OF PHYSIOTHERAPISTS

The Chartered Society of Physiotherapy ("CSP") is incorpor- **7–03** ated by Royal Charter. There are 27,000 chartered physiotherapists in the United Kingdom today, working as individuals or as expert members of a health care team. Although most of the chartered physiotherapists work in the NHS, there are an increasing number now in private practice.

The CSP maintains a register of members and offers those **7–04** members a variety of services including indemnity insurance, legal advice and assistance on any matters arising out of their

105

employment as a chartered physiotherapist. This may include, for example, advice on the disciplinary procedures of the Society itself, or on the procedures of the Physiotherapists Board of the Council for Professions Supplementary to Medicine (see below). The CSP maintains a disciplinary procedure to consider allegations of "professional misconduct" against chartered physiotherapists.

PHYSIOTHERAPISTS BOARD

7–05 This is a statutory authority set up by Act of Parliament, under the Council of Professions Supplementary to Medicine, to regulate the activities of state-registered physiotherapists.

7–06 The Council has a disciplinary procedure to deal with allegations of "infamous conduct" in relation to state-registered physiotherapists. It is possible to pursue a complaint with the CSP and the Physiotherapists Board at the same time. However, after making inquiries, the Chartered Society procedures would be adjourned pending the decision of the Board. If the Board found the practitioner guilty of infamous conduct, then the Society would automatically consider the case under their own procedures. This order is preferable, because the Board operates independently in sorting disciplinary matters and cannot take account of any decision by the Society when hearing the case. The Disciplinary Committee of the Board will deal with the case only upon the admissible evidence put before it. On the other hand, the Society has the discretion to accept as decisive the Board's finding of fact. Even if a practitioner is acquitted by the Physiotherapists Board, the Society will still consider whether any action is needed by the Society.

7–07 The use of professional conduct procedures is not appropriate as a vehicle for securing compensation for any injury deemed to have been caused by physiotherapy. In those circumstances, a civil claim should be considered. A civil claim does not preclude use of either of the two complaints procedures.

7–08 The work of the Council for Professions Supplementary to Medicine is covered in Chapter 13, and therefore the procedure covered in this Chapter will relate to the Chartered Society of Physiotherapy.

NHS COMPLAINTS PROCEDURE

In order to work in the NHS, a physiotherapist must be **7–09** chartered and/or state registered, and anyone wishing to make a complaint about the standards of care provided by a physiotherapist employed within the NHS, should initially utilise the NHS complaints procedures.

However, of the 27,000 chartered physiotherapists currently **7–10** working in the United Kingdom today, there are a significant number now in the private practice industry and sports clinics, and so the relevance of the internal complaints procedures of both the Chartered Society and the Physiotherapists Board arguably have an increasing importance. *N.B.* The Society Disciplinary Procedures were being reviewed in March 1998, although no fundamental changes were envisaged at the time of writing.

PURPOSE OF COMPLAINTS PROCEDURE

The purpose is to investigate allegations of professional miscon- **7–11** duct and to protect the public from a practitioner who may represent a danger.

Before making a complaint to the CSP, a potential complain- **7–12** ant must consider whether the procedure is actually going to provide the outcome he/she is looking for. It is only really worth embarking on a complaint to the CSP if the desired outcome is the removal/suspension of the practitioner's name from the register. Monetary compensation will not be awarded.

PROFESSIONAL MISCONDUCT

The CSP recognises that it is impossible to specify in precise **7–13** terms all those actions which could be deemed to amount to professional misconduct now, and in the future. The Society takes the view that it is for the profession itself to determine what, at any particular time, constitutes conduct requiring disciplinary action by the CSP.

However, the following are examples of misconduct suitable **7–14** for referral to the CSP:

- Criminal convictions
- Disciplinary proceedings by an employer.

- Breach of professional responsibility to a patient, for example failure to provide or arrange appropriate treatment, improper delegation of treatment to unqualified helpers and attempting to carry out procedures to administer drugs in respect of which a practitioner does not have the necessary authority, training or skill.

- Exercise of undue influence over a patient.

- Professional conduct likely to discredit the reputation of the profession, for example misuse or abuse of alcohol, drugs, dishonesty and indecent or violent behaviour.

STRUCTURE FOR DEALING WITH COMPLAINTS

7–15 The CSP has three committees which deal with allegations of professional misconduct and fitness to practice. These are:

1. Preliminary Committee

2. Professional Conduct Committee

3. Health Committee

However, all complaints in the first instance should be made to the Director of the CSP.

WHO CAN MAKE A COMPLAINT

7–16
- The police, following convictions in criminal courts.

- Employers such as health authorities or Trusts.

- Patients/relatives.

- Professional colleagues.

HOW TO MAKE A COMPLAINT

7–17 1. The disciplinary procedure of the CSP can only be invoked if a complainant makes a statutory declaration (a sworn statement) of the facts alleged. The statement must be sworn and signed in the presence of a solicitor or Commissioner for Oaths.

The sort of information and documentation which should be **7–18** included is as follows:-

(i) The name, address and description of the person making the complaint, and the grounds for his/her belief and the truth of any fact declared which is not within his/her own personal knowledge.

(ii) An account of the incident.

(iii) The practitioner's full name and address (if known).

(iv) Description of the practitioner's job at the time of the alleged misconduct.

(v) Description of the location, place and time of the incident.

(vi) If possible the number of staff on duty and the person in charge.

(vii) Witness statements, for example from other staff, friends or relatives.

(viii) Copies of any relevant notes, for example accident forms or correspondence with the employer and details of any police involvement, *e.g.* name and address of the officer in charge.

(ix) Copies of any relevant notes.

2. Upon receipt of a statutory declaration, the Director will **7–19** write to the practitioner notifying him/her of receipt of the information and enclosing a set of the rules regarding the professional disciplinary procedure.

3. The Director will also advise the practitioner of the date of **7–20** the next meeting of the Preliminary Committee to which the case may be referred.

4. The Director will invite the practitioner to respond to the **7–21** allegation made.

5. The Director then submits to the Preliminary Committee **7–22** each case in which an allegation of professional misconduct is received together with any observations received from the practitioner.

PRELIMINARY COMMITTEE

Once the Director has gathered evidence, it is submitted for **7–23** consideration to the Preliminary Committee.

Constitution of the Committee

7–24 The Committee comprises eight members of the Council of the Society, of whom one should not be a member of the CSP. The *quantum* is four.

7–25 The Preliminary Committee is established by the Council and meets not less than three times per year.

7–26 1. The Preliminary Committee investigates all allegations with a view to deciding whether any case ought to be referred for further inquiry by PCC.

7–27 2. Before coming to any view, the Preliminary Committee can ask for further information, either from the member or indeed the complainant.

7–28 3. The complaint has to be considered by the next appropriate meeting of the Preliminary Committee.

7–29 4. The member must be given *28 days'* notice of the meeting at which the Preliminary Committee will consider the complaint against him/her.

7–30 5. The Preliminary Committee meets in private.

7–31 6. The Director sets up and maintains a register of all complaints received and considered by the Committee, and the decision reached.

7–32 7. In situations where no explanation or observation is received from the member, the Committee may, if it thinks fit, make a provisional decision that the case should be referred to the PCC.

7–33 8. If the Director subsequently receives information or a complaint as to another conviction, or as to the conduct of the same member, the chairman of the Preliminary Committee may direct that the former conviction or conduct shall again be referred to the committee together with the subsequent information/complaint. In other words, if a further complaint is made against the same member, then the Preliminary Committee can consider that evidence along with any previous evidence in deciding what course of action to take.

THE POWERS OF THE PRELIMINARY COMMITTEE

The Preliminary Committee may take one of the following **7–34** courses of action:

(a) Refer the case to the Professional Conduct Committee

This will occur if the Preliminary Committee thinks there is **7–35** sufficient evidence to warrant further inquiry or if the member has failed to provide any response to the statutory declaration by the complainant.

(b) Decline to refer the case

The Preliminary Committee may take the view that there is **7–36** insufficient evidence of professional misconduct, in which case the matter will be closed and the CSP member and the complainant informed of the decision.

(c) Refer the matter to the Health Committee

This will occur if the Preliminary Committee takes the view that **7–37** any professional misconduct has arisen as a consequence of the mental or physical ill health of a member.

PROFESSIONAL CONDUCT COMMITTEE

If an allegation is referred by the Preliminary Committee for **7–38** further inquiry, a Professional Conduct Committee ("PCC") shall be constituted.

Constitution of the Committee

- The committee comprises eight members of the Council **7 39** nominated by the Vice-Chairman, of whom the Vice-Chairman will be one.

- Members of the Preliminary Committee cannot also be members of the PCC.

- The PCC must contain one person who is not a member of the CSP.

- All other members will be Fellows or members of the CSP, including a student member.

- One member will be a self-employed physiotherapist.

- Both men and women will be included.

111

- The Vice-Chairman of the CSP shall be the Chairman of the PCC. In the absence of the Vice-Chairman, a substitute chairman will be nominated.

7–40   The PCC has the benefit of advice from a legal assessor who should be a barrister or solicitor of at least 10 years' experience.

7–41   In fitness to practise cases the PCC sits with the assistance of a medical assessor who shall be a principal in general practice or a consultant in an appropriate speciality.

PROCEDURE

7–42   1. A meeting of the PCC will be convened.

7–43   2. *Twenty-eight days'* notice of the meeting of the Committee shall be given to the practitioner.

7–44   3. Notice of inquiry—as soon as the matter is referred to the PCC, the Secretary of the Committee sends the practitioner a "notice of inquiry". This specifies the nature and particulars of the charge against the practitioner and is in the form set out at the end of this chapter.

7–45   The Secretary is the person who sends this to the member. For the notice to be valid, the following rules need to be observed:

- The member needs to be informed of the date, time and place at which the inquiry is to be held.

- The notice of inquiry must be in the requisite form.

- The notice shall be sent by recorded delivery or registered post.

Where there is a complainant, a copy of the notice shall be sent to him/her.

7–46   The practitioner is entitled to appear in person and be represented by counsel or by a solicitor, trade union official, relative or friend, and to adduce evidence, call and cross-examine witnesses and make submissions in reply.

7–47   The complainant may also appear in person and be represented at the hearing by a relative, friend, counsel, or solicitor or by any officer of a professional organisation or trade union.

In the case of a corporate body being the complainant, it may **7–48** be represented by a member or officer of that corporate body duly appointed by the corporate body for the purpose, *e.g.* counsel or a solicitor.

In the event of the practitioner, complainant or corporate **7–49** body deciding to be represented, the CSP must be given *seven days'* notice.

8. Postponement or cancellation of inquiry

The Chairman of the PCC may postpone the inquiry and/or **7–50** refer the matter back to the Preliminary Committee for further consideration as to whether indeed there should be an inquiry.

The Secretary must give all parties who have received a notice of inquiry further notice if there has been a postponement or cancellation.

All parties are entitled to copies of relevant documentation to **7–51** be relied upon at the inquiry, but should make the request known through the secretary of PCC and may also have to pay a copying charge.

It is also open to any party to an inquiry to give any other **7–52** party any documents.

PROCEDURE AT THE INQUIRY

1. If the practitioner fails to attend, then as long as the **7–53** Chairman of the PCC is satisfied that all efforts have been made to give notice, the inquiry is likely to proceed.

2. The charge or charges shall first be read to the PCC. **7–54**

3. It is open to the practitioner to object to either the entire **7–55** charge, or part of the charge made against him/her.

4. After the charges have been read, the practitioner will be **7–56** asked whether he/she admits the facts read.

5. If at any time the members of the PCC feel that amend- **7–57** ments to the charges will be appropriate, then these can be made.

6. Once the charges are made and the practitioner has agreed **7–58** to most, if not all, of the charges, evidence is given in support of the charges and then the practitioner has the right to present his own side of the story and any evidence

in support, or evidence in mitigation to explain the reason for any misconduct.

7–59   *N.B.* The procedure in criminal conviction cases and fitness to practise cases is slightly different. In particular, in criminal investigations, the practitioner is asked to say at the outset whether or not he or she admits to the conviction and then the solicitor or Director will provide evidence of the conviction for any unadmitted offence. It is then open to the practitioner to produce evidence on his/her own behalf. The importance is that the Committee do not accept proven unadmitted convictions on which conclusive evidence is produced by the Director or the solicitor, so the Committee do not rely on the fact that the conviction has been made as prima facie evidence of guilt.

7–60   In relation to conduct or fitness to practise cases, the main difference is that the solicitor, Director or complainant shall open the case against the practitioner and present the facts upon which the complaint or information is based. The solicitor, Director or complainant may then produce evidence of the facts alleged in the charge or charges.

7–61   It is possible for the solicitor, Director or complainant to produce evidence as to the circumstances leading up to the relevant facts and the practitioner's character and previous history. It is also open to the practitioner to produce evidence of the circumstances leading up to the relevant facts and his/her previous character and history.

POWERS OF THE PROFESSIONAL CONDUCT COMMITTEE

7–62   The PCC may take one of the following courses of action:

(a) Reject the complaint

7–63   The PCC may decide that after hearing all the evidence, there is insufficient evidence to find the practitioner guilty of professional misconduct.

(b) Admonish the member and conclude the case

7–64   This would be for a fairly minor offence, where some sanction is recommended and the committee deems that an admonishment is sufficient.

(c) Place the member on probation
In this case the committee effectively postpones making a 7–65
decision for a period of not more than six months and then
meets again at the expiry of that period to determine what
further steps should be taken.

**(d) Impose a condition upon the member's continuing
registration**
In this instance, the committee directs that the practitioner's 7–66
name remain on the register, conditional upon such requirements as the committee may think fit to impose for the
protection of the public, or in the practitioner's own interest.
The condition(s) can only be imposed for a maximum of *three
years*.

(e) Suspend the member from the Register
The member's name will be suspended from the register for a 7–67
maximum of *three years*.

(f) Erasure from the Register
The practitioner's name is erased from the register and there- 7–68
fore he/she can no longer call himself/herself a chartered
physiotherapist.

The chairman of the PCC will announce the decision in 7–69
public, but the deliberations are made in private. Following a
decision by the PCC, if that decision is in any way a sanction
against the practitioner, he/she is invited to address the committee by way of mitigation.

The Secretary then communicates by recorded delivery with 7–70
the member, informing him/her of the decision of the PCC and
any recommendation made by that committee, including any
conditions and requirements and the period of compliance.

In the event that the decision has been suspension or erasure 7–71
from the register, then the practitioner must return to the
Secretary within *21 days* any document issued by the CSP which
indicates registration status The member will be warned that he/
she will be liable to legal proceedings if he/she then holds
himself/herself out to be a member of the register from which
he/she has been erased.

115

APPEALS

7–72 An appeal can be made against erasure or suspension of a practitioner from the register. The grounds of any such appeal should be limited to whether, on the basis of the facts found by the PCC, the penalty imposed was inappropriate.

7–73 An appeal should be sent to the Director of the CSP, and upon receipt of that appeal, an appeals committee should be constituted.

7–74 The committee shall comprise five members of the Council nominated by the Chairman of the Council, of whom the Chairman, if practicable, shall be one. *N.B.* No member of the Preliminary Committee or the PCC who decided the case can sit on the appeals committee.

7–75 The appeals committee shall have power to confirm the erasure or suspension of the member from the register or to substitute a lesser penalty.

7–76 Notice of the appeal shall be given to the CSP within *two months* of the notification of the practitioner of the decision of the PCC.

7–77 The appeals committee must consider the appeal within two months of the receipt by the CSP of the appeal from the practitioner.

7–78 The appeal shall be considered in private.

7–79 If the appeals committee feel that it would be helpful to hear oral evidence, or representations, it can do so.

7–80 The decision of the committee will be communicated to the practitioner.

Application for restoration after erasure

7–81 An application by a practitioner for restoration to the register may be made not less than *12 months* after the erasure or suspension has been considered by the PCC.

FORM OF NOTICE OF INQUIRY

(date)

On behalf of the Chartered Society of Physiotherapy, notice is hereby given to you that in consequence of (a complaint made against you to the Society) or (information received by the Society) an enquiry is to be held into the following charge (charges) against you:

> that, being registered as a member of the Chartered Society of Physiotherapy, you

(If it is a case relating to conviction)

> were on (date) at (specify Court or other body recording the conviction) convicted of (set out particulars of the conviction in sufficient detail to identify the case)

or, (if it is a case relating to conduct)

> (set out briefly the facts alleged) and that in relation to the facts alleged you have been guilty of failure to observe the provisions of the Charter of the Society and the Bye-laws made under that Charter, including the Society's Rules of Professional Conduct or of serious professional misconduct,

or, (if it is a case relating to fitness to practise)

> (set out briefly the facts alleged) and that in relation to the facts alleged your fitness to practise is seriously impaired by reason of your mental or physical condition.

(Where there is more than one charge, the charges are to be numbered consecutively, charges relating to conviction being set out before charges relating to conduct and both being set out before charges relating to fitness ro practise).

Notice is further given to you that a meeting of the Professional Conduct Committee will be held at (date, place and time to be specified, or given later) to consider the above mentioned charge (charges) against you and to determine whether or not they should direct me to erase your name from the Register, or take other steps affecting your registration.

You are hereby invited to appear before the Committee at the place and time specified above, for the purpose of answering the above mentioned charge (charges). You may appear in person or by counsel or solicitor or by any officer or any member of any organisation of which you are a member, or by any friend or member of your family. The Committee have power, if you do not appear, to hear and decide upon the said charge (charges) in your absence.

Any answer, or another statement or communication which you may desire to make with respect to the said charge (charges) should be addressed to me.

If you desire to make any application that the enquiry should be postponed, you should send the application to me as soon as possible, stating the grounds on which you desire a postponement. Any such application will be considered by the Vice-Chairman of the Chartered Society of Physiotherapy in accordance with rule 14 of the Chartered Society of Physiotherapy (Professional Disciplinary Procedures) Rules 1993.

Secretary,
Chartered Society of Physiotherapy

CHAPTER 8

OPTICIANS — THE GENERAL OPTICAL COUNCIL

INTRODUCTION

The Opticians Act 1958, now replaced by the Opticians Act **8–01**
1989, provided for a statutory registration body for opticians.
The latter statute was in fact a consolidating statute to consoli-
date the 1958 Act and its various subsequent statutory amendments and additions. The Act followed recommendations
contained in an unanimous report published in 1952 by a
committee charged with the task of ascertaining whether registration and self regulation was necessary and desirable. The
legislation which followed on from this report provided for a
statutory registration body known as the General Optical Council ("GOC").

The Council has many functions, but generally it is connected **8–02**
with promoting high standards of professional education and
professional conduct amongst opticians. The ways in which the
Council achieves this and which are discussed in this text relate
to:

1. MAINTAINING A REGISTER OF OPHTHALMIC AND **8–03**
DISPENSING OPTICIANS
N.B. Only those registered with the Council can practise in the
United Kingdom.

2. PROMOTION OF HIGH STANDARDS OF TRAINING **8–04**
AND EDUCATION

3. THE PROMOTION OF AN APPROPRIATE ETHICAL **8–05**
STANDARD THROUGHOUT THE PROFESSION AND
OF THE EXERCISE OF DISCIPLINARY POWERS
SHOULD STANDARDS NOT BE MET

8–06   There are two branches of the profession and they have different titles. First, there are optometrists who undertake eye testing and examination, and fit and supply optical appliances. Secondly, there are dispensing opticians who supply and fit optical appliances, but do not test sight.

8–07   It is important to appreciate that the Council does not exist to promote the profession, but to protect the interests of the public by promoting high standards of professional education and conduct within the profession.

COMPOSITION OF THE COUNCIL

8–08   The Council has 28 members of whom eight are nominated by the Privy Council; seven are elected by registered optometrists; three are elected by registered disposing opticians; five are nominated by the examining bodies; one is nominated by the universities training optometrists and four are registered medical practitioners nominated by the Royal College of Ophthalmologists.

8–09   By way of illustration, in 1992 the membership of the Council was made up as follows:

18%   Dispensing opticians or their representatives
21%   Doctors
25%   Lay members
36%   Optometrists or their representatives

N.B. Following a review of the role, functions and responsibilities of the GOC, the composition of the Council is to be revised. With effect from January 1, 1999 the total membership will remain at 28 but they will consist of the following:

32%   Nine lay persons nominated by the Privy Council
21%   Nine optometrists or their representatives, being six elected, two nominated by the College of Optometrists and one nominated by the universities
23%   Six dispensing opticians
14%   Four ophthalmologists nominated by the Royal College of Ophthalmologists

PROFESSIONAL CONDUCT

There are two ways in which the Council maintains and promote **8–10** high standards of professional conduct.

(i) By the exercise of disciplinary functions.

(ii) By making statutory rules to regulate various professional activities and aspects of optical practice.

The College of Optometrists and the Association of British **8–11** Dispensing Opticians give ethical and professional guidance to members, but no definition of professional conduct is provided in the Council's literature. However, it is clear that the Council expects the profession itself to set appropriate standards and to be given guidance in doing so from professional organisations such as the above.

Unacceptable conduct will lead to sanction and although there is **8–12** no definition of this sort of behaviour as such, the disciplinary procedure itself and the decisions of the disciplinary committees provide useful principles to guide the profession, in the same way as the decisions of the courts in civil cases help to establish certain precedents for cases with similar facts/issues.

THE TYPES OF CONDUCT WHICH ARE INVESTIGATED

The following list is by way of example and is not exhaustive: **8–13**

- Criminal convictions, *e.g.* theft from an employer, assault or sexual offences.

- Publicity which offends the Council's rules on publicity, *e.g.* **8–14** an advertisement which includes comparative advertising and therefore refers to the services of a competitor.

- Missed pathology, *e.g.* cases where following a sight test an **8–15** optometrist failed to refer a patient with a detectable abnormality, injury or disease to a medical practitioner. This has been regarded as serious professional misconduct in circumstances where it is not just a question of negligence, but the optometrist has failed to carry out the proper examination which is required.

121

8–16 • Other cases of serious professional misconduct, *e.g.* failure to provide adequate supervision of pre-registration students when holding the post of supervisor.

HOW TO MAKE A COMPLAINT

8–17 Initially, a letter should be written to the Registrar of the General Optical Council—see Appendix A. The letter should set out details of events, witnesses and documentation in support.

STRUCTURE FOR DEALING WITH COMPLAINTS

8–18 The General Optical Council has two committees which deal with allegations of professional misconduct. These are:

8–19 1. Investigating Committee

2. Disciplinary Committee

INVESTIGATING COMMITTEE

8–20 A complaint is initially considered by the Investigating Committee. The essential function of the Investigating Committee is to assess each case to determine whether or not it should be referred to the Disciplinary Committee or to the informal "fitness to practise" procedure.

8–21 The Investigating Committee carries out the following steps:

1. A preliminary investigation of cases where it is alleged that a registered optician/body corporate has done something which may give rise to disciplinary action.

2. A full investigation.

3. The consideration of documentary evidence, namely the complaint and papers in support. This is why it is important to provide these when making a formal complaint.

8–22 The Committee does not call witnesses and does not rely on any oral evidence. A hearing is not held: the Committee simply meets in private to consider the evidence.

POSSIBLE OUTCOMES

(a) Rejection of the Complaint
The Committee decides no further action needs to be taken.   **8–23**

(b) Warning

(c) Referral of the Complaint
The matter is referred to the Disciplinary Committee or to the **8–24** informal "fitness to practise" procedure.

FITNESS TO PRACTISE PROCEDURE
A case is referred to this procedure by the Investigating Committee if that committee feels that remedial action is preferable to disciplinary sanction, *e.g.* where further training is deemed to be required.

DISCIPLINARY COMMITTEE

The Disciplinary Committee hears the evidence and considers **8–25** the case prepared by the Investigating Committee.

1. Documentary evidence already considered by the Investigating Committee is reviewed.

2. A formal hearing is held in public.

3. Rules of evidence similar to a British criminal court are used, for example no hearsay evidence is submitted.

4. The committee has powers to subpoena witnesses or documentation.

5. Oral evidence is given on oath.

6. Legal representation is permitted.

7. The burden of proof is beyond reasonable doubt.

8. The principles of natural justice apply.

9. A practitioner is assumed innocent unless and until he/she is found guilty.

BURDEN OF PROOF

8–26 The Disciplinary Committees applies the criminal standard of proof, *i.e.* beyond reasonable doubt.

TIME LIMIT

8–27 No time limit is given by the Council information booklet but obviously the longer the time lapse between the incident and the complaint, the more difficult the task of investigating the circumstances.

POSSIBLE OUTCOMES

8–28 The Disciplinary Committee will make a disciplinary order if the case is proven. Disciplinary orders can take several forms:

(a) Erasure from the Register

8–29 Removal of the individual or company's name from the list of registered members. This effectively means that the individual or company is not able to practise or continue trading as optician or supplier of glasses, contact lenses, etc.

(b) Suspension Order

8–30 Suspension of the registration of the individual or company for a prescribed period up to a maximum of 12 months.

(c) Penalty Order

8–31 This is when the Committee imposes a fine of not more than £1,600. This can be ordered for each disciplinary matter proved. The money collected in this way goes to the government.

(d) Penalty Order plus Erasure/Suspension

8–32 This would only take place in the gravest of circumstances.

APPEAL

8–33 There is a right of appeal to the Judicial Committee of the Privy Council, *i.e.* the appeal route does not lie with the General Optical Council.

CONCLUSION

8–34 The process operated by the General Optical Council is fairly comprehensive, well-written and easy to understand. However, the Registrar of the Council has pointed out that the statutory disciplinary process relates only to complaints about the conduct of the registrant, and the Council has no statutory power to deal with what may be deemed consumer complaints, *i.e.* those relating to the nature or standard of the goods or services supplied.

Moreover, whilst the orders that can be made by the Disci- **8–35** plinary Committee may appear draconian, the fines imposed are relatively small, particularly if they are being imposed on a body corporate.

It is worth noting that ophthalmic opticians and dispensing **8–36** opticians are required to register with the General Optical Council before they may practice within the United Kingdom. The term "ophthalmic optician" is now rarely used as it is being replaced by the term "optometrist". Therefore, all optometrists are required to register with the Council before they may practise and this is perhaps the biggest safeguard of all. It is open to anyone to check with the Council that an optometrist is registered before commencing a course of treatment or any investigation/eye test.

Ophthalmologists are medical practitioners registered with the General Medical Council and so are not within the jurisdiction of the GOC.

CHAPTER 9

BRITISH CHIROPRACTIC ASSOCIATION

INTRODUCTION

In keeping with the advice contained in the introductory chapter **9–01** of this book, it should be emphasised that it is important to consider only practitioners in this field who are registered with a professional organisation which sets standards of practice, education on training and conduct. There are several organisations concerned with representing or providing a list of "registered" chiropractors.

The organisation whose procedure is described in this book is **9–02** the British Chiropractic Association ("BCA"). The BCA is in fact a company set up to establish a register of practitioners who agree to be bound by the terms and conditions of membership, and in particular, *The Code of Disciplinary Procedure 1992* ("the Code"). This is a document which provides very detailed guidance as to the steps taken to investigate a complaint about a member of the BCA. Copies of all forms in the Code can be found at the end of this chapter.

PURPOSE OF THE CODE

The Code provides procedural rules for the investigation and **9–03** disposal of any complaint alleging that a member of the BCA has been guilty of "misconduct". The Code came into force on May 1, 1992 and applics to all complaints made on or after that date.

MISCONDUCT

The disciplinary code simply says that misconduct is conduct **9–04** contrary to the provisions of the Code of Ethics. Examples include:

- Conviction for a criminal offence.

- Abusive or rude behaviour to patients.

- Breach of confidentiality of a patient's health details.

- Sexual assault on a patient.

WHO CAN MAKE A COMPLAINT

9–05 Anyone with information relating to an experience of misconduct by a member of the BCA can complain to the BCA. Complaints may be received from:

- patients;

- relatives;

- professional colleagues;

- members of the Council of the BCA itself; or

- the police, following criminal convictions.

HOW TO COMPLAIN

9–06 A letter can be sent to the disciplinary officer containing an account of the facts along with any supporting documentation. The disciplinary officer is based at the BCA—see Appendix A.

STRUCTURE FOR DEALING WITH COMPLAINTS

9–07 The BCA has two means of dealing with allegations of professional misconduct. These are:

1. Disciplinary Officer

2. Disciplinary Committee

DISCIPLINARY OFFICER

This is a member of the BCA appointed to the post by the **9–08** Council, whose function is to assess all complaints, act on those within his/her power by referring them to the Disciplinary Committee or, in the event of a civil or criminal matter, to take no action until such proceedings have been investigated and concluded.

PROCEDURE

1. The disciplinary officer assesses the complaint and then **9–09** sends the practitioner (known as the respondent in the Code) a written notice of the complaint, asking for a written reply by a specified date (Notice of Complaint and Requirement to Reply—see Form A).

2. A copy of the notice is circulated to all members of the **9–10** Disciplinary Committee and at the same time a copy of the Code is sent to the complainant.

3. Upon receipt of the written response to the complaint from **9–11** the respondent, the disciplinary officer circulates a copy to all members of the Disciplinary Committee and to the complainant.

4. Upon receipt of the written response or in the absence of **9–12** one, the disciplinary officer can come to a decision about the complaint.

5. Whatever the disciplinary officer decides, he or she must **9–13** send notice of that decision to the complainant, the respondent and all members of the Disciplinary Committee (Notice of Decision—see Form B).

POSSIBLE OUTCOMES

(a) Rejection of the complaint

The disciplinary officer may decide that no further action is **9–14** necessary and close his file.

(b) Admonishment of the respondent

This would occur if the complaint was of a fairly minor nature, **9–15** but the disciplinary officer was satisfied that the complaint was justified.

(c) Imposition of a fine on the respondent

9–16 This is a maximum of £500. This figure is set and revised by the Council. The fine must be paid by a date set by the disciplinary officer.

If the respondent fails to pay the fine, the disciplinary officer can refer the matter to the Disciplinary Committee.

(d) Referral to the Disciplinary Committee

9–17 This is in cases involving more serious complaints which warrant further investigation by the Committee.

DISCIPLINARY COMMITTEE

9–18 The function of the Disciplinary Committee is to consider and determine any complaints or application referred to it by the disciplinary officer.

COMPOSITION AND ADMINISTRATION

9–19 There are five members on the Committee: two lay members and three members of the BCA. It should be noted that the disciplinary officer cannot be a member of the Committee, although he/she will carry out administrative functions on behalf of the Committee.

Meetings of the Committee which take place are called by either the Council or the disciplinary officer. The meetings are heard in private. Minutes are taken. The chairman has a casting vote.

PROCEDURE

9–20 It is worth going through the procedure in some detail because the Code itself is detailed, and it is important to appreciate what will be involved before embarking on a complaint to the Disciplinary Committee because there are a number of steps that need to be taken before the Committee will adjudicate on the complaint. The process is in two stages.

FIRST STAGE—Gathering the Evidence

9–21 Having decided to refer the matter to the Disciplinary Committee, the disciplinary officer has to send notice of referral which will also contain a request for more evidence from the complainant. The notice is sent to the complainant, the respondent, and all members of the Disciplinary Committee (Notice to

Parties of Referral of Complaint to Committee and the Complainant to File Evidence—see Form C).

The complainant must prepare an affidavit, *i.e.* a statement of **9–22** the facts on oath. The affidavit must contain the following information:

(i) The full name and address of the complainant.

(ii) The name and address of the respondent.

(iii) The nature of the complaint.

(iv) Evidence in support of the complaint, including:
- Names and address of witnesses
- Witness statements in support
- Other documentation

N.B. Copies of all the documents should be attached to the affidavit.

(v) The grounds for believing any facts which are not within the complainant's direct and personal knowledge or experience. In other words, any second-hand information in support of the complaint.

Clearly, the Committee does not want to investigate a com- **9–23** plaint thoroughly based on rumour and speculation, but if a complainant has good grounds for believing the chiropractor's behaviour, other than to the complainant, should be taken into account, then details and grounds for believing that information must be supplied.

Upon receipt of the affidavit and evidence in support, the **9–24** disciplinary officer sends a copy to the respondent, plus a notice requiring the respondent to send evidence in reply to the complaint. The respondent's reply must again be in affidavit form and must contain:

(i) The full name and address of the respondent.

(ii) The full name and address of the complainant.

(iii) The nature of the reply—in other words an account of events.

(iv) Evidence in support of the reply, including:

- Names and address of any witnesses
- Witness statements in support of his/her position, if possible.
- Other documents which he/she thinks are, or might be relevant.

9–25   Again, copies of any documents in support of the reply should be attached to the affidavit. upon receipt of the affidavit, the disciplinary officer should send a copy to the complainant.

Failure to Follow Evidence

9–26   If either the complainant or the respondent fail to send affidavit evidence to the disciplinary officer within a specified time, the Disciplinary Committee can dismiss the complaint unless the chairman orders otherwise. If the respondent fails to send a reply within a specified time, the Disciplinary Committee can consider the complaint on the evidence which is available, *i.e.* the complainant's evidence alone.

SECOND STAGE—Assessing the Evidence

9–27   The disciplinary officer having gathered the evidence, the Disciplinary Committee can do one of two things:

1. Form a view on the evidence by meeting and assessing the paperwork and coming to a decision; or

2. Decide to hold an inquiry.

ADJUDICATION BY THE DISCIPLINARY COMMITTEE

9–28   The Disciplinary Committee considers affidavit and documentary evidence in support and decides whether or not the complaint is justified. The Disciplinary Committee can take one of the following steps.

(a) Reject the Complaint

(b) Admonish the Respondent

This occurs for less serious offences.

(c) Impose a Fine

The Committee may fine the respondent a maximum of £3,000.

(d) Hold an Inquiry

The Committee may decide to hold an inquiry with a date fixed 9–29
28 days or more from the date of the Committee's decision. *N.B.*
The disciplinary officer must send written notice of the decision
of the Committee to the complainant and the respondent
(Notice of Decision of Disciplinary Committee—see Form E).

INQUIRY

This is a formal hearing with rules of evidence similar to those 9–30
in a court, *e.g.* evidence is given by affidavit and in person on
oath. Considerable preparatory work is carried out prior to an
inquiry. The administrative aspects are carried out by the
disciplinary officer.

Notice of the inquiry is sent to the complainant and the 9–31
respondent, and to all the members of the Disciplinary Committee who will attend (Notice of Referral of Complaint for
Further Investigation at an Inquiry—see Form F). *N.B.* There
must be at least *42 days* between the sending of the notice and
the inquiry.

DISCLOSURE OF DOCUMENTS

At least *14 days* before the date of the inquiry, all parties must 9–32
send to the disciplinary officer copies of any documents they
intend to rely on at the inquiry which may not yet have been
disclosed/seen by other parties. The complainant or respondent
can demand copies of any documents held by the other party, if
it is truly relevant to the inquiry.

Formal notice must be sent to the party who holds the 9–33
document. A copy of the notice should also be sent to the
disciplinary officer (Notice to Supply a Copy Document—see
Form G). *N.B.* Failure to supply documentary evidence as
above, may mean that the document(s) cannot be used at the
inquiry, although the chairman of the Disciplinary Committee
may allow the document in as evidence, even if it has not
previously been supplied to the other parties.

REPRESENTATION

The respondent/complainant may hear the case in person alone 9–34
or accompanied by a friend or professional adviser. It is likely
that the respondent will be represented by his or her insurers'

solicitors, a point which the complainant may wish to bear in mind when preparing for attendance at the Committee.

9–35 The Disciplinary Committee may postpone or adjourn an inquiry, but written notice must be sent to the respondent/complainant.

9–36 If there is more than one complaint or more than one respondent, it is possible to deal at a single inquiry with all matters, *e.g.* two complaints against the same practitioner.

PROCEDURE AT THE INQUIRY

9–37 The inquiry is held by the Disciplinary Committee. A chairman is appointed by the Committee. In the absence of the regular chairman, the Disciplinary Committee will appoint someone else from its number to act as chair for the inquiry.

9–38 The disciplinary officer opens the proceedings by reading a summary of the complaint and proving that notice of the inquiry has indeed been sent to the respondent and the complainant.

EVIDENCE

9–39 (i) Oral or documentary evidence or a combination of both can be given as the Disciplinary Committee thinks fit.

(ii) The complainant gives his/her version of events first. If the complainant is not present, the disciplinary officer will read affidavit evidence and produce any other supporting documentation; call witnesses, etc.

(iii) The respondent then replies and in his or her absence, the disciplinary officer reads the affidavit and produces any other supporting documentation; calls witnesses, etc. After both sides have given their own account, either side can make further submissions to the Committee, first the complainant then the respondent.

(iv) Witnesses may be called and cross-examined on their evidence.

(v) Any allegation that is admitted will require no further proof.

MITIGATION

If the Disciplinary Committee finds in favour of the complain- **9–40** ant, and against the respondent, then the respondent can address the Committee—at that time—in mitigation of any penalties.

The proceedings are recorded and a transcript of the evidence is taken, and a copy is available from the disciplinary officer at a fee to be determined by him/her.

The Disciplinary Committee can, at any time throughout the inquiry, seek legal advice on any matter.

When all the evidence has been presented, the Disciplinary Committee has to go through a two-stage process in order to reach a decision. The Committee must decide:

(i) Whether all or any aspect of the complaint against the respondent actually amounts to misconduct; and if so

(ii) Whether the complainant has proven that the misconduct took place.

Once the Committee has reached its decision, the complain- **9–41** ant and respondent are informed of whether or not a case of misconduct has been proven and if so, what action the Committee intends to take.

The disciplinary officer has to send all parties notice of the **9–42** decision (Notice of Decision of Disciplinary Committee after Inquiry—Form H).

POSSIBLE OUTCOMES

(a) Dismissal of the complaint

This can occurs where, after an inquiry, the committee consider **9–43** that the complaint is not justified.

The Disciplinary Committee can order a complainant who is another member of the BCA to pay the costs of the complaint process and order sanctions against that member for non-compliance of the request to pay the costs if he/she reneges or refuses.

The Disciplinary Committee cannot make such an order against the complainant who is not a member of the BCA, presumably because they are not in a position to impose a sanction for non-compliance.

(b) Admonishment of the respondent

9–44 This would occur when the Committee are satisfied that there has been misconduct and the complaint is proven, but it is of a fairly minor nature.

An admonition at this stage may be slightly frustrating for the complainant after the lengthy process of an inquiry but it is none the less possible.

(c) Impose a fine on the respondent

9–45 This is a maximum of £3,000 and the Committee can impose sanctions for failure to pay, including suspension from membership of the BCA.

(d) Suspension from membership of the BCA

9–46 A suspension can be anything up to *12 months*.

(e) Removal from the List of Members

9–47 This is when a more serious complaint of misconduct is upheld and results in permanent suspension of membership of the BCA.

(f) Costs order

9–48 The Committee can order the respondent to pay the costs associated with the complaint process, including the complainant's costs. Again, there is a sanction for failure to pay, including suspension of membership.

APPEAL

APPEAL FROM A DECISION OF THE DISCIPLINARY OFFICER

9–49 If either the complainant or the respondent are dissatisfied with the disciplinary officer's decision, they can ask for the complaint to be referred to the Disciplinary Committee. Any request for a referral must be made by the date given by the disciplinary officer in his or her notice of decision. Whilst the complaint is being referred to the Disciplinary Committee, any sanctions against the respondent, *e.g.* a fine, shall have no affect.

APPEAL AGAINST A DECISION OF THE DISCIPLINARY COMMITTEE

If either the complainant or respondent are dissatisfied with the **9–50** decision of the Disciplinary Committee, they may appeal to the Appeals Board. Examples might include a complainant being dissatisfied because, despite proving the complaint, no further action is to be taken against the respondent. The respondent may not be happy with the decision to suspend him or her from the register.

PROCEDURE FOR APPEALS

Composition

Appeals are heard by an Appeals Board. The board is made up **9–51** of five people, including the President of the BCA, two other members of the BCA (having a least 10 years' membership of the BCA), and two lay people. Note that neither the disciplinary officer nor any member of the Disciplinary Committee may sit on the Appeals Board.

The person appealing must send a notice of appeal plus **9–52** reasons why an appeal is being made, *i.e.* grounds for appeal, to the disciplinary officer of the BCA before a specified date (Notice of Appeal—see Form I). Upon receipt of the Notice of Appeal, the disciplinary officer must arrange for the appeal to be heard by the Appeals Board. Once he/she has a hearing date, the disciplinary officer sends a notice of hearing to the respondent and complainant (Notice of Hearing of Appeal—see Form J). Hearings of the Appeals Board are conducted in private. Minutes are kept. The chairman has the casting vote in the event of a dispute.

Once a decision has been made, the disciplinary officer sends **9–53** a notice of decision to all parties (Notice of Decision of Appeals Board—see Form M).

POSSIBLE OUTCOMES

(a) Referral back to the Disciplinary Committee

The matter can be referred back to the Disciplinary Committee **9–54** for re-hearing.

(b) Committee Decisions Confirmed or Varied

The decision of the Disciplinary Committee may be confirmed **9–55** or varied.

137

(c) Costs Order

9–56 The Appeals Board can order the costs of the appeal to be paid by the respondent.

RESTORATION OF MEMBERSHIP

9–57 There is a separate procedure whereby a member can apply for restoration of membership. He/she must wait *six months* after the decision to suspend or remove his/her name from the register.

1. The member has to send to the disciplinary officer a notice of intention to apply for restoration of membership (Notice of Intention to Apply for Restoration of Membership—see Form K) plus documentation in support.

2. The disciplinary officer then organises a further hearing of the Disciplinary Committee.

3. Notice of that meeting is sent to the member.

4. The Disciplinary Committee makes its decision based on documentary evidence, possibly oral evidence by the member, and evidence of the member's conduct since removal/suspension from the register.

5. The member is then informed of the outcome of the restoration hearing.

CONCLUSION

9–58 The positive aspect of the BCA procedure is the level of detail. A possible concern, however, is that a lot of power rests in the appointed disciplinary officer and a complaint can effectively be bought off by a member, if he or she pays a fine. However, the complainant can ask for the complaint to be referred for further investigation if that were to happen.

CHIROPRACTORS: SIMPLIFIED SCHEMATIC OF DISCIPLINARY PROCEDURE

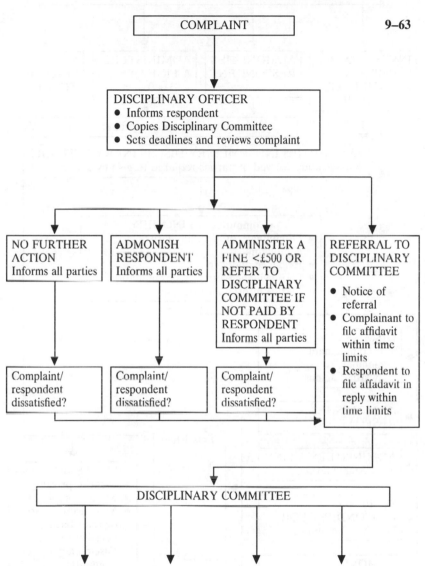

COMPLAINT   9–63

DISCIPLINARY OFFICER
- Informs respondent
- Copies Disciplinary Committee
- Sets deadlines and reviews complaint

NO FURTHER ACTION
Informs all parties

ADMONISH RESPONDENT
Informs all parties

ADMINISTER A FINE <£500 OR REFER TO DISCIPLINARY COMMITTEE IF NOT PAID BY RESPONDENT
Informs all parties

REFERRAL TO DISCIPLINARY COMMITTEE
- Notice of referral
- Complainant to file affidavit within time limits
- Respondent to file affadavit in reply within time limits

Complaint/respondent dissatisfied?

Complaint/respondent dissatisfied?

Complaint/respondent dissatisfied?

DISCIPLINARY COMMITTEE

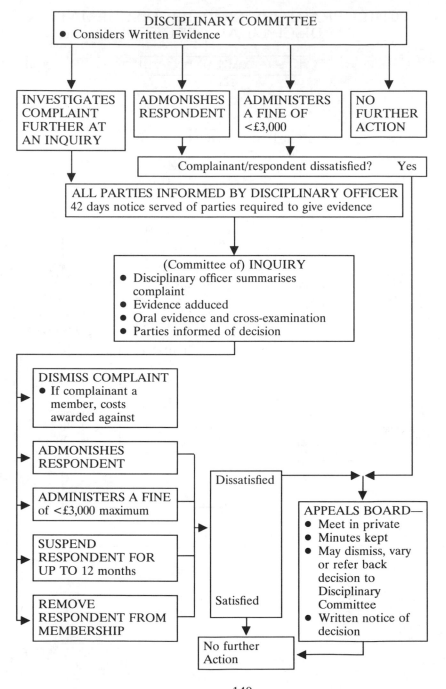

LIST OF FORMS USED IN THE CODE OF DISCIPLINARY PROCEDURE 1992

FORM A Notice of Complaint and Requirement to Reply **9–64**
FORM B Notice of Decision of Disciplinary Officer
FORM C Notice of Referral of Complaint to Disciplinary Committee and for Complaint to File Evidence
FORM D Notice to Respondent to File Evidence in Reply
FORM E Notice of Decision of Disciplinary Committee
FORM F Notice of Referral of Complaint for Further Investigation at an Inquiry
FORM G Notice to Supply a Copy Document
FORM H Notice of Decision of Disciplinary Committee following Inquiry
FORM I Notice of Appeal
FORM J Notice of Hearing of Appeal
FORM K Notice of Application to Restore Membership including Grounds for Application
FORM L Notice of Hearing of Application to Restore Membership
FORM M Notice of Decision of Appeals Board

141

British Chiropractic Association:
Code of Disciplinary Procedure

FORM A

NOTICE OF COMPLAINT AND
REQUIREMENT TO REPLY

Complaint Number:

To:

Date:

1. I enclose a communication dated [date]   which I have received from [name].

2. You will see that the letter contains certain allegations against you.

3. In accordance with the Code of Disciplinary Procedure of the BCA, I require you to give me a written reply to these allegations before [date].

4. On receipt of your reply or after the date specified for making a reply has passed I am empowered to deal with the complaint in one or more of the following ways:
   - (i) to take no further action;
   - (ii) to admonish you;
   - (iii) to refer the complaint to the Disciplinary Committee for further consideration unless you pay a fine to be determined by me but not exceeding the sum of five hundred pounds before a certain date;
   - (iv) to refer the complaint to the Disciplinary Committee for further consideration.

Signed

Disciplinary Officer BCA

142

FORM B

NOTICE OF DECISION OF DISCIPLINARY OFFICER

Complaint Number:

To: The Complainant

The Respondent

Date:

1. In respect of the complaint made by the Complainant against the Respondent the Disciplinary Officer has decided:
   *(i) to dismiss the complaint and to take no further action;
   *(ii) to uphold the complaint that the Respondent was guilty of misconduct in that he/she [here specify misconduct proved] and
   (a) to admonish the Respondent
   (b) to refer the complaint to the Disciplinary Committee unless the Respondent shall pay a fine of £_____ before [insert date]
   *(iii) to refer the complaint to the Disciplinary Committee for further consideration.
   *[Delete and/or complete as required]

2. (i) A Complainant who is dissatisfied with the decision of the Disciplinary Officer to take no further action with regard to his complaint may require the Disciplinary Officer to refer the complaint to the Disciplinary Committee for further consideration.

   (ii) A Respondent who is dissatisfied with the decision of the Disciplinary Officer to admonish him or to refer the complaint to the Disciplinary Committee unless he shall pay a fine before the date specified may require the Disciplinary Officer to refer the complaint to the Disciplinary Committee for further consideration.

Signed

Disciplinary Officer BCA

143

FORM C

NOTICE OF REFERRAL OF COMPLAINT TO DISCIPLINARY COMMITTEE AND FOR COMPLAINANT TO FILE EVIDENCE

Complaint Number:

To: The Complainant

The Respondent

Date:

1. The complaint has been referred to the Disciplinary Committee for further consideration.

2. The Complainant is therefore required to lodge with me before [date]   a sworn affidavit containing the following information:
    (i) his full name and address;
    (ii) the name and address of the Respondent;
    (iii) the nature of his complaint against the Respondent;
    (iv) the evidence on which he intends to rely to support his complaint, including the names and addresses of any witnesses and details of any documents which he believes to be relevant;
    (v) the grounds for his belief in the truth of any fact alleged which is not within his personal knowledge.

3. There must be exhibited to the affidavit of the Complainant copies of any documents referred to in the affidavit and which are in his possession or to which he has access.

4. Failure to lodge the required affidavit before the date specified may result in the dismissal of the complaint by the Disciplinary Committee.

Signed:

Disciplinary Officer BCA

FORM D

NOTICE TO RESPONDENT TO FILE EVIDENCE IN REPLY

Complaint Number:

To: The Respondent

Date:

1. I enclose a copy of the affidavit sworn by the Complainant on [date].

2. You are required to lodge with me before [date] an affidavit in reply to the complaint containing the following information:
   - (i) your full name and address;
   - (ii) the nature of your reply to the complaint;
   - (iii) the evidence on which you intend to rely to support your reply, including the names and addresses of any witnesses and details of any documents which you believe to be relevant;
   - (iv) the grounds for your belief in the truth of any fact alleged which is not within your personal knowledge.

3. There must be exhibited to your affidavit copies of any documents referred to in the affidavit and which are in your possession or available to you.

4. Failure to lodge the required affidavit before the date specified will result in your complaint being considered by the Disciplinary Committee on the evidence available.

Signed

Disciplinary Officer BCA

FORM E

NOTICE OF DECISION OF DISCIPLINARY COMMITTEE

Complaint Number:

To: The Complainant

The Respondent

Date:

1. In respect of the complaint made by the Complainant against the Respondent the Disciplinary Officer has decided:
   *(i) to dismiss the complaint and to take no further action;
   *(ii) to uphold the complaint that the Respondent was guilty of misconduct in that he/she [here specify misconduct proved] and
      (a) to admonish the Respondent
      (b) to order the Respondent to pay a fine of £_____
         before [insert date]
   *(iii) to investigate the complaint further at an Enquiry on a date to be fixed.
   *[Delete and/or complete as required]

2. If the Complainant is dissatisfied with the decision of the Disciplinary Committee to take no further action, he may appeal to the Appeals Board.

3. If the Respondent is dissatisfied with the decision of the Disciplinary Committee to admonish him, or to order him to pay a fine, he may appeal to the Appeals Board.

4. Notice of appeal shall be given to the Disciplinary Officer in Form I before [insert date] and shall be accompanied by written submission setting out the grounds for the appeal.

Signed

Disciplinary Officer BCA

FORM F

NOTICE OF REFERRAL OF COMPLAINT FOR FURTHER INVESTIGATION AT AN INQUIRY

Complaint Number:

To: The Complainant

   The Respondent

Date:

1. The complaint by the Complainant against the Respondent will be investigated further at an Inquiry to be held by the Disciplinary Committee at [venue]   on [date]   at [time].

2. You are required to attend the Inquiry and to give evidence in support of/in reply to the complaint.

Signed

Disciplinary Officer BCA

FORM G

NOTICE TO SUPPLY A COPY DOCUMENT

Complaint Number:

To: *The Complainant

    *The Respondent

    The Disciplinary Officer

From: *The Complainant

    *The Respondent

*[Delete as appropriate]

Date:

1. The Complainant/Respondent requires the Respondent/ Complainant to supply him with a copy of the following documents relevant to the complaint made by the Complainant within 7 days of receipt of this notice:
   [list documents]

2. The Complainant/Respondent undertakes to pay the proper charges for the said documents.

3. A copy of this notice has been served on the Disciplinary Officer.

Signed

The Complainant/Respondent

FORM H

NOTICE OF DECISION OF DISCIPLINARY COMMITTEE FOLLOWING INQUIRY

Complaint Number:

To: The Complainant

The Respondent

Date:

*1A. In respect of the complaint made by the Complainant against the Respondent, the Disciplinary Committee has decided to dismiss the complaint *and to order the Complainant to pay costs amounting to £   on the terms set out in paragraph 2 below.

*1B. In respect of the complaint made by the Complainant against the Respondent the Disciplinary Committee has decided to uphold the complaint that the Respondent was guilty of misconduct in that he/she [here specify the misconduct proved] and:
  *(i)   to admonish the Respondent
  *(ii) to order the Respondent to pay a fine of £_____ on the terms set out in paragraph 2 below
  *(iii) to suspend the Respondent from membership of the British Chiropractic Association for a period of   months
  *(iv) to direct that the Respondent shall cease to be a member of the British Chiropractic Association forthwith
  *(v)   to order the Respondent to pay costs amounting to £_____ on the terms set out in paragraph 2 below.
*[Delete and complete as appropriate]

2. The fine and the costs shall be paid by the Complainant/Respondent in a single payment/in instalments of £_____ each payable on or before the following dates: [specify dates]

Failure to pay the fine and/or costs as ordered shall result in the automatic suspension of the Complainant/Respondent from membership of the British Chiropractic Association until further order of the Disciplinary Committee.

3. If the Complainant is dissatisfied with the decision of the Disciplinary Committee to take no further action, and/or to order him to pay costs he may appeal to the Appeals Board.

4. If the Respondent is dissatisfied with the decision of the Disciplinary Committee to uphold the complaint and to impose the penalty or penalties set out in paragraph 1B above he may appeal to the Appeals Board.

149

5. Notice of Appeal shall be given to the Disciplinary Officer in Form I before [date] and shall be accompanied by written submissions setting out the grounds for the appeal.

Signed

Disciplinary Officer BCA

FORM I

NOTICE OF APPEAL

Complaint Number:

To: The Disciplinary Officer

Date:

1. The Complainant/Respondent appeals to the Appeals Board against the following decision of the Disciplinary Committee:
   [state decision]

2. The grounds of the appeal are set out in the accompanying submissions.

Signed

The Complainant/Respondent

FORM J

NOTICE OF HEARING OF APPEAL

Complaint Number:

To: The Complainant

The Respondent

Date:

1. The Complainant/Respondent has appealed to the Appeals Board. A copy of the Notice of Appeal is enclosed.
2. The Appeal will be considered by the Appeals Board at its meeting on [date].
3. You will be notified of any directions given by the Appeals Board and of its decision in due course.

Signed

Disciplinary Officer BCA

FORM K

NOTICE OF APPLICATION TO RESTORE MEMBERSHIP INCLUDING GROUNDS FOR APPLICATION

Complaint Number:

To: The Disciplinary Officer

Date:

1. By a decision of the Disciplinary Committee on [date]   it was directed that I should cease to be a member of the British Chiropractic Association.

2. I hereby apply for my membership to be restored.

3. The grounds for my application are as follows:
    [state grounds[

4. The evidence which I intend to produce in support of my application is as follows:
    [state evidence]

Signed

The Respondent

FORM L

NOTICE OF HEARING OF APPLICATION TO RESTORE MEMBERSHIP

Complaint Number:

To: The Respondent

Date:

1. The hearing of your application for the restoration of your membership of the British Chiropractic Association will take place at [venue] on [date] at [time]

2. You are required to attend the hearing to give evidence in support of your application.

Signed

Disciplinary Officer BCA

FORM M

NOTICE OF DECISION OF APPEALS BOARD

Complaint Number:

To: The Complainant

The Respondent

Date:

In respect of the Appeal made by the Complainant/Respondent the Appeals Board has decided as follows:
[state decision]

Signed

Disciplinary Officer BCA

155

CHAPTER 10

SPEECH THERAPISTS—
THE ROYAL COLLEGE OF SPEECH
AND LANGUAGE THERAPISTS

INTRODUCTION

Speech and language therapists work to assess and treat those **10–01** who have who have problems understanding/using language, for example those with a stammer, or swallowing difficulties. Some people are born with these problems or they may acquire them after an accident or illness, for example a road traffic accident involving head injuries, or a stroke or other degenerative condition such as Parkinson's disease. They also work with parents, carers and other health professionals, such as teachers, nurses and doctors as part of a multi-disciplinary team.

The profession is keen to point out that communication **10–02** covers many activities and not just speaking. For example, communication can include listening, speaking, reading and writing. Speech and language therapists work in hospitals, mainstream and special needs schools, community health centres and day centres, and indeed in people's own homes. Some are in independent practice.

In order to qualify, a person must undertake a three to four **10–03** year degree course or a two year postgraduate degree. There are a number of courses throughout the country, but to be valid a degree must be obtained from a course accredited by the Royal College of Speech and Language Therapists. The College is the organisation which maintains a register of qualified speech and language therapists who have passed examinations on accredited courses. Those in independent practice can join the Association of Speech Therapists in Independent Practice, who are affiliated to the College. There is also a separate Managers Association.

10–04 The College publishes a leaflet entitled *Professional Competence—Complaints Procedure* which is available from the address given in Appendix A.

10–05 The basic qualification for a speech and language therapist is a BSc—Bachelor of Science in Clinical Communications and/or an RCSLT which means that the practitioner is a registered member of the Royal College of Speech and Language Therapists.

10–06 It should be noted that registration with the college is voluntary and not statutory, but that all members working in the NHS are governed by statute and must behave in accordance with NHS guidelines because the NHS is ultimately their employer.

10–07 It is important that anyone providing treatment of this kind has a commitment to a high level of professional competence, and it is therefore advisable to ensure that a treating therapist is registered with the Royal College of Speech and Language Therapists. If there is any doubt it is always possible to telephone the College and ask if the practitioner's name is included on the register.

10–08 The College states in its leaflet that maintenance of a high standard of ethical and professional conduct is essential both for the welfare of clients/patients and for the reputation of the profession.

10–09 The complaints procedure is seen as a way of helping maintain a high standard of competence because those not doing so are reported, complaints are fully investigated and the practice of the member can be improved if necessary.

TYPE OF COMPLAINT

10–10 • Professional competence/negligence.

• Professional conduct in terms of adherence to the Code of Ethics.

• Conviction of a criminal offence.

• Fraud—this might be dealt with at a local level, for example by the NHS employer but it might also be serious enough to also warrant referral to the professional body.

TIME LIMITS

Complaints should be made within *six months* of the alleged **10–11** incident. However, in some circumstances longer may be allowed by the Professional Director of the College.

WHO CAN MAKE A COMPLAINT

- Any member of the public.   **10–12**

- Any member of the College who is concerned about the conduct of another member.

- A local health authority/Trust.

- Community health councils.

- The police, following a criminal conviction.

STRUCTURE

1. PROFESSIONAL DIRECTOR

The Professional Director of the College of Speech and Lan- **10–13** guage Therapists deals with complaints and is responsible for the initial screening of complaints. Basically, there are two ways in which complaints are handled by the Professional Director.

> (i) Informal—Conciliation
> (ii) Formal

2. SCREENING COMMITTEE

3. PROFESSIONAL COMMITTEE

HOW TO COMPLAIN

PRE-COMMITTEE STAGE
Considerable attempts are made to resolve complaints by way of **10–14** investigation and conciliation. This pre-committee stage is handled by the Professional Director. Exceptions would be very serious complaints which may be referred straight to the Screening Committee.

159

INFORMAL PROCEDURE

10–15 Initially, attempts will be made to deal with the complaint informally.

10–16 1. Complainants should make the complaint to the practitioner orally or in writing. If there is no response, or the response is perceived to be inadequate, then the complainant should write to the Professional Director at the College of Speech and Language Therapists setting out the facts giving rise to the complaint.

10–17 2. Initially, the Professional Director will look at the evidence and then instigate a process of conciliation to try and resolve the dispute. This means that both sides meet in the presence of a conciliator who will listen to each side of the argument and then suggest a solution which may be acceptable to both sides.

10–18 3. If the conciliation is successful then both the complainant and the practitioner sign an agreed statement setting out the nature of the complaint and the outcome/decision and how the matter was resolved.

10–19 4. The file will then be closed.

10–20 5. The procedure must be concluded within *six months* of the date that the Professional Director receives notice of formal written complaint.

FORMAL PROCEDURE

10–21 If informal resolution is not going to be possible then the complainant will need to make a formal complaint.

10–22 1. This has to be in writing and addressed to the Professional Director of the College of Speech and Language Therapy.

10–23 2. The complaint must include a statement setting out the facts and grounds for the complaint, and must be signed.

10–24 3. The complaint must be acknowledged by the Professional Director within *14 days*.

10–25 4. The Professional Director must inform the practitioner of the complaint within *14 days* of receipt of the complaint.

10–26 5. Notification of the complaint must include a summary of the complaint.

INVESTIGATION

1. The Professional Director carries out an initial assessment **10–27** of the complaint and asks the practitioner to comment in writing on the allegations that have been made.

2. The Professional Director then considers the evidence on **10–28** both sides and may decide at this stage that there are no reasonable grounds to complain, advise the complainant and practitioner of this decision, and close the file.

3. However, the Professional Director may consider that the **10–29** complaint should be investigated further, either by referring the matter to the Screening Committee or by recommending conciliation.

CONCILIATION

1. Again, both sides are asked to meet in the presence of a **10–30** conciliator.

2. Each side gives their own case. **10–31**

3. The conciliator may make recommendations as to a poss- **10–32** ible solution or try and get the parties to identify a solution themselves.

4. If the parties do agree and a decision is made, then they **10–33** should prepare a statement including a brief summary of the facts that have given rise to the complaint and the decision that has been made.

COMMITTEE STAGE
This stage is also organised by the Professional Director who is **10–34** responsible for ensuring that meetings of committees take place as required. He/she also has to present the case to the Professional Committee.

SCREENING COMMITTEE
If the complaint is not resolved either through the informal or **10–35** formal process, or conciliation, or indeed if the complaint is very serious, then it will be referred to the Screening Committee and the Professional Director will call a meeting of the Screening Committee to deal with the complaint.

PROCEDURE

10–36 A meeting of the Committee must be called within *two months* of receipt of the formal complaint.

10–37 1. All the parties are notified in writing of the date, time and place of the meeting at least *35 days* in advance of the meeting.

10–38 2. The Professional Director acts as chairperson for the meeting.

10–39 3. Any information given at the hearing is to be treated as strictly confidential.

10–40 4. Both sides should provide written submissions.

10–41 5. There need to be at least three members of the Committee plus the Professional Director and two members of the Council for each hearing.

POSSIBLE OUTCOMES

10–42 (a) **Case Dismissed**

10–43 (b) **Referral to the Professional Committee**
The Screening Committee reviews the evidence and either decides to refer the complaint to the next stage, *i.e.* to the Professional Committee, or not, for one of the following reasons:

(i) The Screening Committee does not agree that the complaint needs further action.

(ii) The Screening Committee thinks, despite what the parties may feel, that conciliation is appropriate, or that although the matter has already been through a conciliation meeting which was not successful, a second attempt might be successful, in which case the matter is referred back to the Professional Director to arrange conciliation either for the first time or again.

(iii) The complaint has arisen as a result of ill-health on the part of a practitioner, in which case it would be better dealt with by the practitioner's occupational health department, employer or union.

(iv) Both complainant and practitioner are notified of the decision of the Screening Committee within *14 days*.

PROFESSIONAL COMMITTEE

If the Screening Committee refers the complaint to the Profes- **10–44** sional Committee, the Professional Director will advise the chairperson of events to date.

1. The chair of the Professional Committee convenes a meet- **10–45** ing of the Committee.

2. The chair is not allowed to be a member of the College, **10–46** and will be a lay person appointed by the College to chair these meetings.

3. A meeting of the Professional Committee must be **10–47** arranged within *two calendar months* of the meeting of the Screening Committee (if possible).

4. Written submissions are requested from the complainant **10–48** and practitioner, and must be sent to the Professional Director and received by him/her within *21 days* of the hearing.

5. The written submissions are then circulated to members of **10–49** the Committee and all the parties involved.

6. At the hearing, the Professional Director presents the case **10–50** on the part of the College. He/she is entitled to take legal advice.

HEARINGS

There are no formal rules of evidence. Evidence may be **10–51** received from all parties, either oral or written that the Committee feel would be helpful in coming to a decision.

The disclosure of any documentation supplied in support of **10–52** either side's case is only disclosed at the discretion of the chairman or the Professional Committee.

Questions can be asked at the Committee, and the parties can **10–53** ask each other questions.

The complainant/practitioner can be assisted by a friend, **10–54** trade union representative, but may not be represented or assisted by a lawyer acting within a professional capacity.

The chairman must ensure equal/fair treatment of the complainant and the practitioner.

DECISION

10–55 The Professional Committee considers all the evidence and makes a decision which is set out in a concluding statement. The Professional Committee can decide as follows:

10–56 **(a) No further action**

(b) Censure without suspension/removal from the Practice Register

10–57 This occurs when a complaint is upheld but is not serious enough to warrant suspension or removal from the register.

(c) Censure with permission to remain on the Register

10–58 The Committee may prescribe conditions and timescales by which the conditions may be met, in order for the practitioner to remain on the register. The College keeps a record of the censure and any conditions and timescales. The censure is for a period specified by the Committee.

A censure can be removed after the specified period, *i.e.* the College amends the record.

(d) Suspension

10–59 This involves temporary removal of a practitioner from the register with prescribed conditions and timescales in which the conditions must be satisfied.

(e) Removal from the Register

10–60 This is for an indefinite period.

- Conditions and timescales are included in the concluding statement of the Professional Committee.

- Suspension/removal from the register is published in a bulletin of the college.

- All known employees and clients are informed in the event of a removal from the register.

- All known employers and clients are informed if the Committee orders a censure or suspension.

- In the event that the Professional Committee decides that no further action is necessary, then the practitioner can inform his employer and any clients of the findings of the Committee.

Both complainant and practitioner are advised of the decision and the right to appeal.

MODIFICATION OF DECISION

Prescribed conditions and timescales for re-admission to the register may be modified by the Professional Committee which may in turn delegate this power to the Professional Director or chairman of the Professional Committee. The modification will presumably be in the practitioner's favour because it is only the practitioner who can apply for modification, which will be considered if he/she can show "good cause". **10–61**

APPEALS

There is a right of appeal by a practitioner/complainant against the findings of the Professional Committee. A practitioner who has been removed or suspended from the register can also appeal, but not against censure. **10–62**

1. The appeal must be lodged with the Professional Director within *28 days* of notification of the Professional Committee's decision. **10–63**

2. The appeal body is made up of the chairman of the Ethics Committee of the College, chairman of the Council of the College, and a member of the Ethics Committee and three members of the Council who have not been members of the Screening or Professional Committee. **10–64**

3. The appeal body is chaired by the chairman of the Council. **10–65**

4. An appeal can only be made against a sanction imposed or a breach of the formal procedure, and is not an opportunity to re-hear the case. **10–66**

RESTORATION

A practitioner can apply for restoration to the register.

10–67 1. The practitioner must set out in writing the reasons why his/her name should be restored.

10–68 2. The matter is considered by the Council at its next meeting.

10–69 3. The practitioner is informed of the decision of the Council within *14 days* of the Council meeting at which the matter is considered.
N.B. The complainant would not normally be advised of an application for registration to the register or the outcome of the application.

COSTS

10–70 The college emphasises that it will not pay travel or any other expenses incurred by either party to the complaint.

CONCLUSION

10–71 There is a well thought out procedure organised by the College for those wishing to complain about the practice of its members. The procedure differs from many others because of the emphasis on a thorough investigation prior to referring the matter to a committee. The use of conciliation is also unusual but accords with the increasing interest in alternative dispute resolution (see Chapter 1). The self-imposed time limits are extremely strict and might cause problems if there were to be an increase in the number of complaints.

CHAPTER 11

HOMOEOPATHS—SOCIETY OF HOMOEOPATHS

INTRODUCTION

Homoeopaths as a profession are not regulated by Parliament, **11–01** therefore anybody can practise homoeopathy. Those practitioners working within the NHS are regulated by the NHS rules regarding standards of employees, but otherwise the regulation of the profession is on a voluntary basis.

There are several organisations which provide courses leading **11–02** to qualification as a homocopath and a system of registration and regulation of qualified members.

The organisation covered in this text is the Society of **11–03** Homoeopaths. The Society recognises training courses which meet its educational standards and maintains a register of members which is published and updated regularly. The Society takes the view that the maintenance and publication of a register of qualified and experienced homoeopaths helps the public to obtain first class homoeopathic treatment. A copy of the register is available on request from the Society at the address at Appendix A.

The Society's main four functions are as follows: **11–04**

1. MAINTAINING AND PUBLISHING A REGISTER OF MEMBERS

The register contains the names of over 600 members, all of **11–05** whom have been examined by the Registration Committee of the Society. Members are issued with a Certificate of Registration and they use the initials RSHom. or FSHom.—see Appendix B.

In addition to understanding the philosophy of homoeopathy, **11–06** members must also agree to be bound by the Society's *Code of*

167

Ethics and Practice. A copy of this document is also available from the General Secretary, Society of Homoeopaths. As well as registered members, the Society has some licensed members who have undertaken courses at other colleges which are recognised by the Society but have not yet completed the full registration criteria. Licensed members still need to satisfy the Society's own criteria and demonstrate competency in professional practice.

2. EDUCATION AND TRAINING

11–07 The Society states that in order to be registered members must have all been adequately trained in "the essential medical sciences and skills", and have had suitable clinical training and experience.

3. MAINTAINING HIGH STANDARDS OF PRACTICE

11–08 The Society ensures that all members have sufficient professional experience in the practice of homoeopathy in order to justify the confidence of the Society in recommending them.

4. THE PROMOTION OF HOMOEOPATHIC PHILOSOPHY

11–09 The members should practise according to the principles established by Samuel Hahnemann, founder of homoeopathy, and must have a proper understanding and knowledge of homoeopathic philosophy.

CODE OF ETHICS AND PRACTICE

11–10 The Society publishes a *Code of Ethics and Practice* ("the Code"), the purpose of which is twofold.

(i) To establish and maintain standards of homoeopathy.

(ii) To guide and inform members of the public seeking homoeopathic treatment.

11–11 All insured members of the Society of Homoeopaths are required to abide by the Code and student members are advised to familiarise themselves with the standards as set out in the Code, in preparation for practice. The guiding principles of the

Society, as stated in the code, are to encourage integrity and responsibility in the practice of homoeopathy. This includes having regard for the needs of the patient, the reputation and advancement of homoeopathy, and the development of understanding amongst homoeopaths.

N.B. The "guiding principles" form the basis for discussion in **11–12** consideration of any complaint against a homoeopath. In other words, whilst there may not be a definition of misconduct or a clear indication of what justifies a legitimate complaint about treatment, it is clear that if a homoeopath acts in contravention of the Code, that will be a factor which is borne in mind in deciding whether a complaint is justified and whether a member should be sanctioned by the Society in some way.

The Code identifies 11 points which illustrate how the general **11–13** guiding principles apply to the behaviour of a practitioner:

"1. The homoeopath's highest and only calling is to make sick people healthy, to heal, as it is termed (according to Hahnemann).

2. A homoeopath shall be guided by ethical principles **11–14** in all matters regarding professional practice, and conduct their practice with integrity and dignity.

3. The highest standards need to be observed in con- **11–15** duct and in the care of the patient.

4. The homoeopath owes loyalty to the patient and **11–16** should have regard for their wishes.

5. The homoeopath shall recognise that the patient is in **11–17** charge of their own health. The homoeopath shall encourage each patient to take increasing responsibility for their own healing and learning.

6. A homoeopath shall practise with integrity and com- **11–18** petence any skills other than homoeopathy as they may think appropriate, in a course of treatment. They shall make it clear to the patient concerned the nature of the treatment offered and indicate their relevant qualifications for the practise of such skills.

7. Homoeopaths are responsible for continuing their **11–19** personal and professional development by undertaking supervision, conferring with colleagues, and acquiring knowledge of new theory and practice through further training and study.

11–20   8. Homoeopaths need to monitor their competence and be aware of the necessity to consult with colleagues or to refer a patient to a suitably qualified and experienced practitioner.

11–21   9. It is important that homoeopaths support and assist each other in their study and practice.

11–22   10. Homoeopaths should not disparage nor speak disrespectfully of fellow homoeopaths in public, to patients or to students.

11–23   11. Homoeopaths shall report research findings and clinical experience methodically, honestly and without distortion. All speculative theories should be stated as such and clearly distinguished."[1]

PURPOSE OF THE COMPLAINTS PROCEDURE

11–24 The purpose of the complaints procedure is three-fold.

1. To deal formally with complaints made against a licensed or registered member of the Society which cannot be resolved informally by way of discussion or correspondence.

11–25   2. To ensure the impartial investigation of a complaint against a licensed or registered member of the Society.

11–26   3. To ensure the full investigation of a complaint and to prevent recurrence.

N.B. This is not a punitive process, but one which seeks to ensure the impartial and full investigation of a complaint, correct any poor practice and prevent the same mistake happening again.

WHO CAN COMPLAIN

11–27 Any member of the public who has received treatment he/she considers unacceptable, or indeed any member of the profession who is concerned about the standard of care provided by another practitioner.

[1] Reproduced with kind permission of the Society of Homoeopaths.

TYPES OF COMPLAINT

- Concerns about the defectiveness of treatment and/or **11–28** ongoing support.

- Breach of confidentiality, in particular disclosure of information to a third party, *e.g.* a GP or relative.

- Alleged sexual abuse.

This list is not exhaustive and obviously a variety of complaints are received by, or reported to, the Society.

BURDEN OF PROOF

It is for the complainant to establish whether the standard of **11–29** care or the acts or omissions of the practitioner amount to misconduct, and if so, whether they actually occurred. The Code does *not* give a definition of a burden of proof, *e.g.* beyond reasonable doubt.

HOW TO COMPLAIN TO THE SOCIETY

A complainant should send a letter and supporting documenta- **11–30** tion to the Professional Conduct Director setting out grounds for complaint.

PROCEDURE

STAGE I—INFORMAL COMPLAINTS PROCEDURE

A patient who wishes to complain about a member's treatment **11–31** could firstly write to the homoeopath concerned to see whether a reasonable explanation is forthcoming, or even make an appointment to discuss, face to face, their concern. The patient may wish to take a friend or relative along for moral support.

Alternatively, the patient may write to the Society—to the **11–32** Professional Conduct Director (PCD) at the Society's address— and explain the problem. The patient may receive a satisfactory explanation or reassurance from the PCD that the matter rests at this stage.

However, in cases involving more serious complaints, or ones **11–33** which are not capable of informal resolution, perhaps because after entering into correspondence with the practitioner, and/or the Society, the patient is still not satisfied, he/she should move on to the formal complaints procedure.

STAGE II—FORMAL PROCEDURE

11–34 The Society has two means of dealing with complaints via the formal procedure. These are:

1. Preliminary Investigation

2. Adjudication Panel

PURPOSE OF THE FORMAL PROCEDURE

11–35 The purpose is really twofold, to ascertain as fully as possible the facts surrounding a complaint and to make sure that complaint is thoroughly investigated, but equally importantly, the purpose of the procedure is to prevent the same thing happening again.

1. PRELIMINARY INVESTIGATION

11–36 This is carried out by the Professional Conduct Director who asks the complainant and the practitioner to provide sufficient information to enable a swift and thorough investigation of the complaint. The Professional Conduct Director's role is described as conciliator/mediator between the complainant and the practitioner, to help them reach an agreed resolution. *N.B.* This is in complete contrast to many other complaints procedures covered elsewhere in this book, where the emphasis is not on conciliation or mediation.

11–37 To do this the Professional Conduct Director or delegated member of the Professional Conduct Sub-committee takes the following steps:

1. He/she obtains all the relevant facts from both sides.

2. He/she keeps both parties regularly informed of the fact that there has been a complaint at all, and what he/she is doing about the complaint.

3. He/she clarifies any misunderstandings on both sides.

4. He/she mediates between both sides to see if a resolution is possible.

At the end of the investigation, the Professional Conduct Director will try and ensure that mistakes are acknowledged and rectified.

POSSIBLE OUTCOMES

Following the preliminary investigation, the Professional Con- **11–38**
duct Director must do the following:

(a) Inform Parties
Inform the complainant of the outcome of the investigation as **11–39**
soon as possible.

(b) Summarise the complaint
In the case of complex or potentially serious complaints a **11–40**
summary of the complaint and his/her findings must be presented at the next meeting of the Board of Directors of the
Society. Confidentiality is maintained at all stages.

(c) Refer to Next Stage
The matter can be referred to the Adjudication Panel if **11–41**
appropriate.

2. ADJUDICATION PANEL

If a complaint is too serious to be dealt with at the preliminary **11–42**
investigation or the complaint cannot be resolved by way of
mediation/conciliation, then the Professional Conduct Director
has to refer the matter to the next stage, *i.e.* the Adjudication
Panel. This means that the complaint can be further investigated
and each side's case put to a panel of adjudicators at a formal
hearing.

Administration
Panel Hearings are organised by a convenor who is appointed by **11–43**
the Professional Conduct Director. His/her duties include:

- Appointing a panel of adjudicators.

- Keeping all parties informed of the procedure, because all
  documentation is going to be sent to the convenor who will
  then distribute it to all those concerned.

- Keeping good order throughout the preparation for an
  attendance at the hearing itself.

- Ensuring fairness throughout.

Composition

11–44 The Adjudication Panel consists of five members of the Society—two to four members of the Society and one lay person who is *not* a homoeopath but is an acknowledged expert in his or her field. The panel is chosen by the convenor from the full membership and the lay person from a list, held by the Professional Conduct Director, of lay people willing to sit on these hearings.

11–45 Two further points should be made about the panel composition, as it is unusual.

(i) All members must agree to attend the hearing when they are appointed and to observe full confidentiality.

(ii) Care is taken to ensure, as far as possible, that the gender and ethnic origin of any party to the proceedings is reflected amongst the panel members.

11–46 At least *seven days'* notice of the hearing is sent to the complainant and the practitioner in accordance with the articles of association, and the notice must include the following:

- date

- time

- place

- nature of complaint

- right to representation

11–47 Both sides are asked to submit documentation not previously disclosed to the convenor, at least *21 days* before the hearing.

11–48 The complainant and the practitioner can be represented at the hearing by either a friend or a professional adviser. When either party is to be represented, the convenor must inform all the other parties of this fact and whether the representative is a professional adviser.

11–49 This is to ensure equal representation if possible or at least that one side is not hijacked by the other party bringing a professional adviser of whom they had no advance notice.

The Hearing
This is a formal hearing, with a chairman being appointed. **11–50**
Panel members:

- hear both sides' evidence;

- ask relevant questions;

- consider new evidence;

- ask specialist advice of any aspect of the complaint or the treatment is not clear;

- withdraw to consider the case; and

- prepare a written report of findings for submission to the Board of Directors.

Decision
This must be notified with a report to the Board of Directors **11–51** within *28 days* of the hearing.

The panel of adjudicators must decide whether or not a **11–52** member of the Society is guilty of misconduct or incompetence, both or neither. That is the essence of the decision that they are going to be making.

The panel must indicate the grounds for the decision based **11–53** on a breach of the Code and the articles of association. In other words, if a member is going to be punished or sanctioned, then the panel must show how the practitioner has deviated from the Code.

At the conclusion of the hearing, the panel may give advice/ **11–54** make suggestions to the directors concerning the conduct of a member, even if the complaint is dismissed—in other words, if the panel considers that the complaint was probably not indicative of an incompetence or misconduct on the part of the member, but there were grounds for concern or procedures needed to be changed to avoid a similar incident happening again.

Notwithstanding the above, the Code makes it clear that the **11–55** Adjudication Panel hearings should be conducted in a relaxed and open style. Again, this is in complete contrast to many of the other complaints procedures considered elsewhere in this book.

POSSIBLE OUTCOMES

(a) Adjournment

11–56 If a member, or indeed the complainant, fails to turn up for the hearing, the hearing may be adjourned, but if either party fails to turn up a second time then the hearing will probably go ahead in that person's absence, unless there is a good reason for their absence.

(b) Postponement of the Decision

11–57 In this case the hearing goes ahead, but the Panel postpones making a decision until a later date, either because it would like more evidence, or possibly for another administrative reason, or because it would simply like more time to consider the particular facts of the case.

(c) Adjudication on the same day

11–58 Whatever decision the Panel makes—even if it is to postpone making a decision or an adjournment—a written report must be submitted to the convenor within *28 days* of the adjudication hearing.

POWERS OF THE ADJUDICATION PANEL

(a) To issue a first warning

11–59 An example would be a relatively minor matter which had not caused "harmful effects", but was nonetheless a valid complaint.

(b) To issue a further warning

11–60 This is where a member has already had a first warning and is now issued with a further warning.

(c) To issue a final warning

11–61 This is where a member continues to behave in a way that gives rise to complaints and is just what it says, namely a final warning before more serious action is taken.

11–62 *N.B.* All warnings must include the following:

(i) Details of the behaviour, act or omission which the practitioner is being warned about.

(ii) What improvements are required.

(iii) How they will be measured.

(iv) The length of time the warning will be in place.

(v) The consequences of not heeding the warning.

(d) To reprimand the member
This is where a member is reprimanded by the Society for **11–63** conduct unbecoming to a member. The complaint may be proven but is not of a particularly serious or dangerous nature.

(e) Written undertaking
This is for repeated failure to heed warnings and a written **11–64** undertaking is demanded instead of a suspension being ordered. This is where a member has either been guilty of persistent poor behaviour or there is a serious complaint about the member, in which case he/she is obliged to give a written undertaking to the Society that he/she will not re-offend again.

(f) To suspend membership
This is obviously for more serious cases where the complaint is **11–65** justified and the practitioner is considered to be a danger to the public. The suspension is for up to *two years in total* and is where the member has been shown to be unfit to practise, or is in need of further treatment or training and has persisted in practising without undertaking further training or correcting the poor practice despite earlier action taken by the panel to warn or reprimand or demand an undertaking to do so.

(g) Expulsion from membership
This is the most serious penalty, and is a last resort given as a **11–66** consequence of gross incompetence or misconduct. This is for the most serious complaints only. It means that the member is effectively expelled from membership of the Society. The expulsion is for an indefinite period.

PROCEDURE FOLLOWING DECISION BY THE PANEL

1. Upon receiving the report and the decision of the panel, **11–67** the convenor shall present them to the Professional Conduct Director for ratification by the directors at the next board meeting. Only a simple majority of directors is required to ratify the decision.

11–68 2. Within *seven days* of receiving notice of the ratification of the directors on the panel's decision, the convenor needs to notify the result in writing to the complainant and to the practitioner. If there is a decision not to ratify, *i.e.* the Board of Directors does not accept the panel's decision, then the matter is referred back to the panel for its reconsideration. In that event, the practitioner and the complainant are informed. If the directors refuse to ratify a second time after receiving the second report, the practitioner will have a ground for appeal.

APPEALS

11–69 Appeals are administered not by the convenor or the Director of Professional Conduct, but by the Secretary of the Society.

11–70 1. When the convenor informs the complainant and practitioner that the decision of the panel has been ratified by the Board of Directors, he must also notify the member of the right to appeal.

11–71 2. Within *28 days* of receiving a notice of the right to appeal, the practitioner can write to the Secretary of the Society giving notice of his/her intention to appeal against the decision of the panel and giving grounds for the appeal.

11–72 3. Grounds for appeal may be one of the following:
   (a) There is further evidence which was not available at the panel hearing.
   (b) There is evidence that procedures were not properly followed.
   (c) The practitioner considers that he/she has been unjustly or unfairly treated in the adjudication process.
   (d) The directors have twice refused to ratify the panel decision.

11–73 4. The practitioner can supply no more than 1,000 words in support of the appeal, and this document should be sent to the Secretary within *28 days* of the notice of intention to appeal.

5. Within *three calendar months* of receipt by the Society of **11–74** the notice of the intention to appeal, the Secretary must convene an appeal meeting.

6. The Secretary has to write to the appellant, *i.e.* the person **11–75** making the appeal, at least *21 days* before the date of the meeting, giving the following information:
   - time
   - date
   - place
   - right to be represented

7. Appeal meetings consist of not more than 12 full members **11–76** of the Society. They are chosen from the full membership and are given notice of the appeal, and the grounds for appeal, *21 days* before the date of the meeting. Members are asked to reply indicating whether or not they are willing to attend the appeal. From these replies, the Secretary selects 12 full members who cannot be directors or members of the original adjudication panel. The Secretary chooses the appeal panel by way of lots. If there are insufficient volunteers to sit on the appeal panel, extra members will be drawn by lot from the whole membership, excluding directors or panel members as before, and asked to attend the meeting.

8. A chairperson is elected who will conduct the proceedings **11–77** and ensure fairness and good order throughout.

9. Meetings are held in private. A clerk is appointed in **11–78** advance to record the proceedings.

10. The member will be entitled to be legally or otherwise **11–79** represented and can provide a written statement in support of the appeal and call evidence from witnesses, etc. on his/her own behalf.

11. The Professional Conduct Director presents the case **11–80** against the practitioner. Again, he/she may send out a written statement of not more than 1,000 words with the notice of the meeting, can supply additional written evidence in support of the case against the practitioner, and may call witnesses and be represented. All the documentary evidence will need to be made available to the practitioner at least *21 days* before the meeting.

11–81 12. Each side presents their case, and then each side is allowed to sum up their respective case. The appeals panel will then withdraw and either decide the matter there and then or adjourn, but usually the decision is made at the time and the parties are recalled to hear the decision. This is subsequently confirmed in writing. In the event of there being a delay in making the decision, then the decision must be made within *14 days* of the meeting.

11–82 13. The decision is made on the basis of a three-quarters majority. In the absence of such a majority, the decision of the panel ratified by the directors will be set aside and the case against the practitioner dismissed.

11–83 As can be seen, the appeals process does not automatically involve complainants. A practitioner who wishes to appeal may get the decision of the adjudication panel overturned and return to the position he/she was in before the complaint.

CONCLUSION

11–84 From the available literature this procedure seems slightly less formal than others, with emphasis on conciliation and less formal hearings. Time limits for the various steps are designed to ensure that complaints are dealt with swiftly without foregoing the right of both the complainant and the practitioner to have the complaint thoroughly and fairly investigated and adjudicated. The literature produced by the Society of Homoeopaths is particularly easy to read and follow.

HOMOEOPATHS: SIMPLIFIED SCHEMATIC OF DISCIPLINARY PROCEDURE

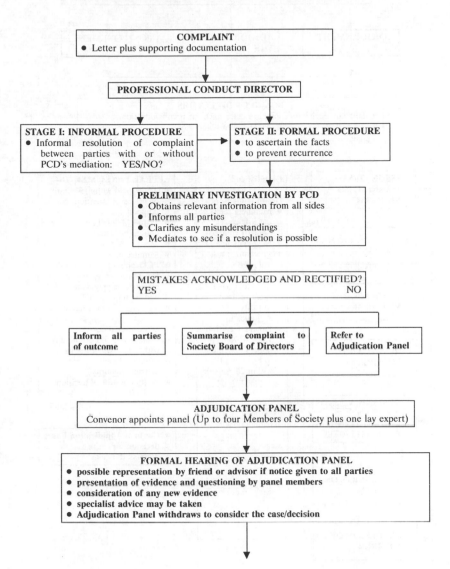

COMPLAINT
- Letter plus supporting documentation

PROFESSIONAL CONDUCT DIRECTOR

STAGE I: INFORMAL PROCEDURE
- Informal resolution of complaint between parties with or without PCD's mediation: YES/NO?

STAGE II: FORMAL PROCEDURE
- to ascertain the facts
- to prevent recurrence

PRELIMINARY INVESTIGATION BY PCD
- Obtains relevant information from all sides
- Informs all parties
- Clarifies any misunderstandings
- Mediates to see if a resolution is possible

MISTAKES ACKNOWLEDGED AND RECTIFIED?
YES   NO

Inform all parties of outcome

Summarise complaint to Society Board of Directors

Refer to Adjudication Panel

ADJUDICATION PANEL
Convenor appoints panel (Up to four Members of Society plus one lay expert)

FORMAL HEARING OF ADJUDICATION PANEL
- possible representation by friend or advisor if notice given to all parties
- presentation of evidence and questioning by panel members
- consideration of any new evidence
- specialist advice may be taken
- Adjudication Panel withdraws to consider the case/decision

181

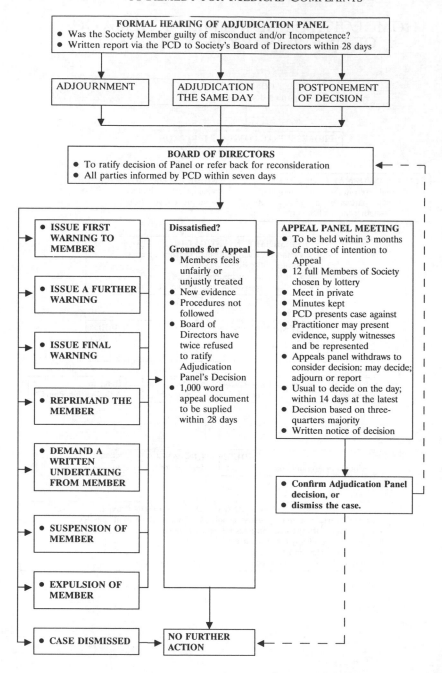

FORMAL HEARING OF ADJUDICATION PANEL
- Was the Society Member guilty of misconduct and/or Incompetence?
- Written report via the PCD to Society's Board of Directors within 28 days

ADJOURNMENT

ADJUDICATION THE SAME DAY

POSTPONEMENT OF DECISION

BOARD OF DIRECTORS
- To ratify decision of Panel or refer back for reconsideration
- All parties informed by PCD within seven days

- **ISSUE FIRST WARNING TO MEMBER**

- **ISSUE A FURTHER WARNING**

- **ISSUE FINAL WARNING**

- **REPRIMAND THE MEMBER**

- **DEMAND A WRITTEN UNDERTAKING FROM MEMBER**

- **SUSPENSION OF MEMBER**

- **EXPULSION OF MEMBER**

- **CASE DISMISSED**

Dissatisfied?

Grounds for Appeal
- Members feels unfairly or unjustly treated
- New evidence
- Procedures not followed
- Board of Directors have twice refused to ratify Adjudication Panel's Decision
- 1,000 word appeal document to be suplied within 28 days

APPEAL PANEL MEETING
- To be held within 3 months of notice of intention to Appeal
- 12 full Members of Society chosen by lottery
- Meet in private
- Minutes kept
- PCD presents case against
- Practitioner may present evidence, supply witnesses and be represented
- Appeals panel withdraws to consider decision: may decide; adjourn or report
- Usual to decide on the day; within 14 days at the latest
- Decision based on three-quarters majority
- Written notice of decision

- **Confirm Adjudication Panel decision, or**
- **dismiss the case.**

NO FURTHER ACTION

CHAPTER 12

ACUPUNCTURISTS—BRITISH ACUPUNCTURE COUNCIL

INTRODUCTION

Acupuncturists as a profession are not governed by statute and **12–01** anyone can practise as an acupuncturist. There is no government register. However, there are various professional bodies which operate an accreditation and registration system. The one which will be covered here is the British Acupuncture Council, whose Executive Committee prepares and publishes a Code of Ethics and a Code of Practice which are updated from time to time.

The purpose of these two codes is twofold: **12–02**

(a) To lay down standards of conduct in practice expected of a registered member; and

(b) To give advice in relation to the practice of acupuncture.

The Code of Practice is not just concerned with misconduct; it also provides rules for dealing with allegations about a member's health, criminal convictions and clinical standards.

MISCONDUCT

In the Code, this is described as unacceptable professional **12–03** conduct. Examples include:

- Conduct which falls short of the standard required of an acupuncture practitioner.

- Conviction of a criminal offence.

- Physical or mental illness which renders the member incapacitated.

PURPOSE OF PROCEDURE

12–04 To maintain standards of practice and ensure members are fit to practise and conduct themselves in a manner appropriate to the profession.

WHO CAN COMPLAIN

12–05 • Members of the public.

• Members of the Council, or indeed any members of the profession.

• The police, following a criminal conviction.

HOW TO COMPLAIN

12–06 A letter setting out grounds for complaint should be sent to the Registrar of the Council at the address given in Appendix A. The letter should include a factual account of what happened with any supporting documentation or witness statements, etc.

STRUCTURE

12–07 1. Preliminary Investigation Committee

2. Professional Conduct Committee

3. Health Committee

4. Executive Committee

12–08 These are known collectively as the Ethical Committees, and again are set up by the Council to deal specifically with complaints about members' conduct.

The Executive Committee writes and updates the Code of Ethics and Code of Practice (see paragraph 12–01 above).

PRELIMINARY INVESTIGATION COMMITTEE

12–09 Any complaint received by the registrar will be passed to this committee for initial assessment. It should be noted that the Preliminary Investigation Committee ("PIC") comprises three members of the Executive Committee, who are known as "screeners". As the name suggests, their task at this stage is to screen complaints and decide whether or not they should move to the next stage.

PROCEDURE

1. Details of the complaint/allegation will be entered onto a **12–10** register.

2. A notice of the complaint will be sent to the practitioner who has *28 days* to respond.

3. The committee members then consider all the evidence about the allegation or complaint including the practitioner's response.

4. The PIC may wish to hear the respondent's side of the story, in which case a hearing will be organised at which the practitioner can be represented.

5. The committee then decides whether further action is necessary.

6. Any finding by the committee is entered on a register.

7. The complainant will be notified of any decision by the committee.

POSSIBLE OUTCOMES

(a) Decision that no further action is necessary
This will occur where, for example, a complaint proves to be **12–11** unsubstantiated, or a criminal conviction gave rise to an investigation, but the offence was not actually related to the practitioner's work as an acupuncturist.

(b) Referral to the appropriate Committee
In this case the PIC decides there is a case to answer, in which **12–12** circumstance the matter is referred either to the Health Committee or the Professional Conduct Committee ("PCC").

Professional Conduct Committee

12–13 The matter is referred to this committee if a complaint has been made regarding a member's conduct.

Health Committee

12–14 A matter is referred to the Health Committee if a query has been raised about the member's ability to practise due to physical/mental ill health.

(c) Interim Suspension

12–15 Such an order is only made if a practitioner is a danger to the public. The Preliminary Proceedings Committee ("PPC") can order the Registrar to suspend a member for a period of *not more than four weeks*.

12–16 Orders by the PPC.

- No order can be made by the PPC once the matter has been referred to the Health Committee or the PCC.

- The PPC cannot make more than one order.

- Before making an order the PPC must allow the practitioner the opportunity to give his or her own version of events or provide a defence, at a hearing at which the practitioner is entitled to be represented.

PROFESSIONAL CONDUCT COMMITTEE

COMPOSITION

12–17 The committee consists of three members of the Executive Committee plus possibly two other members of the Council who are co-opted to join.

PROCEDURE

12–18 1. The committee considers the allegation/complaint and/or the information supplied by the PIC and then decides whether to make any orders or conditions on the member's registration.

2. Rules are decided by the Executive Committee.

3. The practitioner is given notice of the meeting of the committee or the hearing date.

4. The practitioner will have the opportunity to put forward his/her case as long as he/she informs the committee that he/she intends to do so, within *28 days* of receiving the notice of hearing.

5. There will only be a hearing if the committee thinks it is desirable to hold one.

6. Evidence will be given orally and on oath, and any documentation supplied by either party will be considered by the committee.

7. The practitioner can be legally represented.

8. A legal assessor is appointed to give advice to the PCC.

9. The hearing will be in public unless it is considered to be in the interest of the complainant or the practitioner that the evidence be in private.

10. The decision of the committee will be notified to the practitioner along with the reason for the decision and details of the right of appeal.

POSSIBLE OUTCOMES

(a) Admonishment of the member
This will occur in relatively straightforward cases where the **12–19** misconduct is not particularly serious.

(b) Imposition of a Conditions of Practice Order
This is an order imposing conditions on a practitioner with **12–20** which he/she has to comply whilst practising as an acupuncturist. Such a condition can only be imposed for a maximum of *three years*. During the lifetime of such an order, the committee may:

- Revoke the order or extend or reduce the period for which the order is effective.

- Revoke or vary the conditions.

- Order a test of competence to be taken and passed by the practitioner before he/she can be reinstated.

187

12–21   If a first application for a variation to an order is refused, then the practitioner cannot apply again for at least *12 months*.

12–22 (c) Removal from the register

APPEALS

12–23 A member may appeal against an order for an interim suspension.

PROCEDURE

12–24   1. An appeal must be lodged within *28 days* of the order being made.

2. The practitioner must set out the grounds for the appeal, *i.e.* why the order was inappropriate or should not have been made.

REVOCATION

12–25 An interim suspension order can be revoked by the PCC on the basis that there has been a change of circumstances. Such an application must be made within *six months* of the original order or the first appeal.

NON-COMPLIANCE

12–26 It is an offence for a practitioner not to comply with an order of the PIC, the PCC or the Health Committee.

HEALTH COMMITTEE

12–27 Matters will be referred to the Health Committee if the allegation includes a query as to the practitioner's fitness to practise due to ill health.

PROCEDURE

12–28   1. A private meeting will be held between the practitioner and the members of the committee.

12–29   2. Medical assessors will be appointed to the Health Committee by the Executive Committee in order to investigate the case.

3. The Health Committee consists of three members of the **12–30** Executive Committee plus at least one registered medical practitioner who may also be a member of the Executive Committee of the Council.

POSSIBLE OUTCOMES

(a) Removal of name from the Register
The member may be advised that his/her name will be removed **12–31** from the register due to ill health, or conditions may be imposed on his/her continuing membership, for example that he/she seek medical treatment.

(b) Interim Suspension Order
An interim suspension order may be made in the meantime if **12–32** the practitioner is deemed to be a danger to the public.

(c) Case dismissed **12–33**

APPEALS

1. An appeal must be made within *28 days* of the Health **12–34** Committee's decision.

2. An Appeals Tribunal will be set up by the Executive Committee and will include the chairman of the Council and two members of the Council, one of whom will be a director.

3. The Executive Committee set out rules regarding appeal and these are sent to practitioners following a decision by the Health Committee.

4. An appeal of this kind will usually be held in public.

5. Evidence given may include some of the evidence given at the original hearing, but also supplemental and additional information provided since the decision of the Health Committee.

6. The Executive Committee can stand in as the practitioner or members of the committee can put themselves in the complainant's shoes.

7. The Appeals Tribunal can affirm the Health Committees decision or go one step further, for example it may order an interim suspension order even if that was not initially ordered by the Health Committee.

8. The Appeals Tribunal can award costs against the practitioner or to the practitioner if it thinks fit.

CONCLUSION

The BAC procedure is not the easiest to follow but they have now produced "Informal Guidelines" (March 1998) which can be found at the end of this Chapter.

BRITISH ACUPUNCTURE COUNCIL

INFORMAL GUIDELINES — MARCH 20, 1998

Information for Complainants and Practitioners

Please note: this information supersedes all previous publications produced by the BAcC.

The function of the Ethics Committees (Preliminary Investigating Committee (PIC) and Professional Conduct Committee (PCC)) is to consider and take appropriate action regarding official complaints lodged against a practising member after the procedures, as given in this Information sheet, are satisfied. All decisions are made by committee and both the PIC and PCC consist of experienced member practitioners and impartial member(s) of the public. All complaints are initially considered and dealt with by the PIC but where necessary, the case may be referred to the PCC. Although the British Acupuncture Council (BAcC), as a governing body, supports its members in all other matters, the members of the PIC and PCC have to remain neutral to both the complainant and practitioner when a complaint is being considered. The relevant committee instructs the Ethics Secretary on all appropriate correspondence and action. For confidentiality purposes, all correspondence sent to the BAcC should be addressed to the **Ethics Secretary.**

Please note that the British Acupuncture Council office staff, the Ethics Secretary and the individual members of the PIC and PCC do not have the authority to pass comment or give information over the telephone to either the complainant or practitioner.

1. If a patient simply wishes to register a complaint verbally or in writing but without taking any further action, a record is made in the Confidential Complaints Book detailing the names of both the complainant and the practitioner, the date and brief details of the nature of the complaint.

2. If the complainant wishes the complaint to be considered by the PIC, the complainant will be sent this information sheet together with copies of the BAcC Code of Ethics and Code of Professional Conduct.

191

3. The complainant is then required to provide a full written statement of the complaint and confirm to the BAcC, in writing, that:
    (a) They understand the procedures detailed in this sheet.
    (b) They authorise in investigation to be undertaken.
    (c) In the course of the investigation full statements may be copied to either party for comment.

CHAPTER 13

PROFESSIONS SUPPLEMENTARY TO MEDICINE—COUNCIL FOR PROFESSIONS SUPPLEMENTARY TO MEDICINE

INTRODUCTION

The Council for Professions Supplementary to Medicine ("the **13–01** Council") was set up by an Act of Parliament—the Professions Supplementary to Medicine Act 1960.

The new shorter *Oxford English Dictionary* defines profession **13–02** as "a vocation, a calling, especially one requiring advanced knowledge or training and some branch of learning, or science". In the Council's introduction to state registration, it says:

"In order to belong to a profession, an Applicant must have had an appropriate period of training, obtained the requisite qualifications and be willing to accept and conform to disciplinary standards that have been set by the profession's regulatory body."

Medicine has always been an evolving science, but the last 30 years has seen a huge growth in the diversity of treatment available and the complexity and sophistication of that treatment. This in turn has led to a much wider range of specialist staff becoming involved in the provision of health care. Several of these have developed their own professional associations and their practice has since been regulated under the Professions Supplementary to Medicine Act 1960.

Practitioners of the following professions are currently mem- **13–03** bers, although other professional organisations are considering joining:

193

- Chiropody

- Dietetics

- Medical laboratory science

- Occupational therapy

- Orthoptics

- Physiotherapy

- Radiography

- Arts therapy (three separate groups: art, drama and music therapists)

- Prosthetics and orthotics

STRUCTURE

13–04 The organisation operates a two-tier but non-hierarchical system.

THE COUNCIL

13–05 The Council is an independent body external to, and independent from, the individual professions and associations, and from the NHS and the Department of Health. Council membership consists of representation from each profession, the Royal Colleges and the General Medical Council, as well as the Department of Health and individuals appointed by the Privy Council. There are 27 Council members.

13–06 One way of explaining the Council, which was used in the Council's *Annual Report* for 1987/1988, is that the organisation is like a group of commercial companies with the Council acting as a holding company having responsibility for the group's finance and its corporate image. Thus the Council is the enabling mechanism within which the subsidiaries operate—the subsidiaries being the Boards.

BOARDS

13–07 The Boards regulate their own affairs under the auspices of the Council. There are presently nine professions which affiliated to the Council, and each of these professions has its own Board.

Boards vary in size according to the number of members in the profession itself. There is a direct correlation between the size of the profession and the size of the Board.

COMPOSITION

The first category of members is made up of those who are **13–08** nominated and elected by the registered members of the profession. The second category is made up of medical practitioners and others appointed by the Council after nomination by the Royal Colleges and, depending on the Board, one or two members nominated by a variety of appropriate bodies. The elected representative members, *i.e.* the first category, have a majority of one over the second category. To ensure that this is always the case, *i.e.* at each meeting, every elected member is elected as part of a pair so that at least one of the pair will attend each meeting.

FUNCTIONS

BOARDS

The Boards are not there to advance the interests of the **13–09** professions; rather their main aim is to protect the public. They do this by registration and regulation. Their main functions are therefore as follows:

1. TO ORGANISE STATE REGISTRATION OF QUALIFIED MEMBERS OF EACH PROFESSION

This includes vetting potential registrants and maintaining and **13–10** publishing a list of registered members.

2. TO REGULATE THE STANDARDS OF EACH PROFESSION

This is achieved by a variety of means: **13–11**

(i) Approving higher education institutions as being suitable to run approved programmes.

(ii) Validating and monitoring training courses for professions supplementary to medicine as being suitable to lead to state registration.

(iii) Vetting potential registrants to ensure that they are suitably qualified.

(iv) Preparing and publishing a register of members who are state registered.

THE COUNCIL

13–12 The Council's task is to facilitate and organise state registration for members of professions supplementary to medicine. Specifically its function is as follows:

(i) To provide a focus for each of the Boards who form the federation.

(ii) To maintain an overview the work of the Boards, but not to veto any action taken—the Boards are independent of the Council, as indeed the Council is independent of the Boards.

(iii) To act as a forum for discussion and debate, and to influence decision-making regarding health care issues, for example, changes in NHS funding, state registration for professions supplementary to medicine, and the interaction between doctors and allied health care professions, such as proper delegation of responsibility, autonomy and recognition of the professional status of allied professions.

(iv) To provide resources for the Boards, for example administrative support, which is paid for by the registration fee.

(v) To organise central training for those visiting and evaluating courses for each profession.

(vii) Disciplinary matters—each Board appoints from its members an Investigating and a Disciplinary Committee, whose duty is to prepare a Statement of Conduct for each profession which contains a definition of "infamous" conduct.

(viii) Protection of title—prosecution can be brought against a professional claiming to be registered who is not.

13–13 *N.B.* At the time of writing the arrangement for protection of title for some of the professions is unsatisfactory, insofar as anyone can call himself/herself a physiotherapist or an occupational therapist despite not being registered. It can be difficult to ascertain whether any given practitioner has been on an appropriate training course, and is suitably qualified to provide treatment.

The best way to find out if someone is state registered is to telephone the Council and ask. The address and telephone number are given in Appendix A. It should also be noted that it is an offence under the Professions Supplementary to Medicine Act for anyone not registered with the Council to claim to be.

DISCIPLINARY FUNCTIONS OF THE BOARD

The Professions Supplementary to Medicine Act 1960 provides **13–14** that each Board must establish two committees:

1. Investigating Committee
2. Disciplinary Committee

Section 9(6) of the Act states: **13–15**

"It is the duty of each Disciplinary Committee to prepare and from time to time revise, in consultation with its Board and Council, a statement as to the kind of conduct which the Committee considers to be infamous conduct in a professional respect . . ."

A copy of the statement is sent to each member after each revision.

A statement of conduct is a statutory document which indicates **13–16** the conduct needed to avoid the kind of conduct which a disciplinary committee considers to be "infamous conduct in a professional respect". A statement of conduct also contains guidance on the sort of standards expected. For example, most say that a practitioner must be competent to do whatever he/she claims to be able to do.

The disciplinary committee draws up these statements inde- **13–17** pendently of the Boards, which have no say or veto over the contents but must, together with Council, be consulted.

It is interesting to note that the disciplinary committee is **13–18** independent of the Board, and the Board is independent of the Council. This is a system of checks and balances operated by the Council structure to try and ensure independence and objectivity in all matters relating to the regulation and registration of a profession supplementary to medicine.

INFAMOUS CONDUCT

13–19 This is defined as relating to the deliberate endangering or adverse affecting of a patient and the abuse of the professional/patient relationship. *N.B.* Infamous conduct is not about incompetence. It is about rude, aggressive or above all dangerous behaviour.

13–20 Anyone wishing to allege that a practitioner is incompetent would probably be better advised to proceed with a complaint by way of the NHS complaints procedure if the practitioner is an NHS employee, or by approaching the manager/administrator in the case of a private institution. It should also be noted, however, that the distinction between infamous conduct and incompetence can become blurred in cases arising from ill health or due to repeated/continuous incompetence.

TYPES OF COMPLAINT

13–21 Examples of infamous conduct or dangerous behaviour in 1995/1996 include:

- A radiographer charged with infamous conduct for failing to check properly the identity of an x-ray, thereby causing it to be incorrectly ascribed to the wrong patient. The radiographer's name was initially removed from the register and later restored.

- A chiropodist charged in a civil court under the Act for advertising in a sensational manner and for displaying a certificate stating that he was a member of the Society of Chiropodists and Podiatrists, which was not true. The case was proven.

- A medical laboratory scientific officer charged with infamous conduct for claiming to possess a degree qualification, which was not true.

- A successful prosecution under the Professions Supplementary to Medicine Act of someone claiming to be a state registered physiotherapist when she was not. A fine was imposed by magistrates.

WHO CAN COMPLAIN

- Members of the public.   **13–22**

- Solicitors on behalf of clients.

- The police, by providing a certificate after a criminal conviction (though not in every case). *N.B.* Contrast this with the position in relation to doctors and the General Medical Council where the police automatically refer criminal convictions to the GMC. There is no automatic referral to the Council for Professions Supplementary to Medicine.

- Health authorities and Trusts.

- Managers and employers outside the NHS.

- Professional colleagues.

PROCEDURE

1. A formal complaint should be made in writing to the   **13–23**
   Registrar of the Council, whose address can be found at Appendix A.
   (i) If the complaint is made by a member of the general public or a colleague who is not the manager of the register then it must be made by way of a statutory declaration which is a statement made on oath and sworn before a solicitor or commissioner for oaths.
   (ii) If on the other hand, the complaint is being made by a personnel director or employer, then a letter plus supporting evidence will be sufficient.

In either case, the following information should be included: **13–24**

- The name and address of the practitioner and their qualifications, if known.
- The name and address of the complainant and occupation.
- Date, time and place of the alleged incident.
- Any other relevant information including the names of any witnesses or documentation in support of the complaint.

13–25 2. The practitioner is informed of the fact that there has been a complaint and what it is about, and is invited to comment.

13–26 3. The Registrar initially assesses the complaint to see whether or not the respondent is state registered, whether or not the conduct falls within the scope of the Act and whether or not sufficient information has been provided and whether the papers are in order, and obtain further information if required. Then he/she passes the complaint to the Investigating Committee.

INVESTIGATING COMMITTEE

13–27 The Committee is made up of members of the Board. The majority are elected, but others are appointed by other bodies such as the Royal Colleges. The size of the Investigating Committee for each Board depends upon the size of the Board. For example the Physiotherapists Board has 21 members, 11 of whom sit on the Investigating Committee. A smaller Board would have much smaller numbers of members of the Investigating Committee.

13–28 Members of the Board who sit on the Investigating Committee cannot also sit on the Disciplinary Committee.

1. Once the Registrar is satisfied that the complaint should be referred to the Investigating Committee, he/she asks the Secretariat of the Council to arrange a date for the Investigating Committee to meet.

2. The quorum for an Investigating Committee is three.

3. Meetings of the committee are held in private.

4. The members deliberate on the evidence and come to a decision.

POSSIBLE OUTCOMES

(a) No case to answer

13–29 This is in instances where there is insufficient evidence of infamous conduct or where the conduct is not thought to be relevant to the respondent's professional status, or where on balance, the respondent appears to have committed no offence. The practitioner and the complainant are informed that the complaint will not be taken further.

(b) Request for more information
The committee may decide that there is insufficient evidence or **13–30** information in supportof the complaint, but the members would like more information before forming a final view. In these situations, the committee will ask the Council's solicitor to seek more information from the party.

(c) Referral to the Disciplinary Committee
If the Investigating Committee is satisfied that there is sufficient **13–31** information or evidence to justify further investigation, the matter will be referred to the Disciplinary Committee. All parties are informed of the fact that the matter has been referred.

DISCIPLINARY COMMITTEE

1. The Investigating Committee sends all the documents to **13–32** the Council's solicitor who carries out further investigations, including possibly interviewing the parties and seeking further documentary evidence, witness statements and medical reports if appropriate.

2. When he/she is ready he/she will ask the Secretariat to arrange a date for the Disciplinary Committee to meet.

3. The procedures of the Disciplinary Committee usually take place at the head office of the Council.

4. The solicitor for the Council is also present and puts the Board's case, *i.e.* the Board's position if a question of misconduct is to be heard.

5. The practitioner may have a solicitor to represent him/her, or indeed may be absent and still be represented by a solicitor.

6. A legal assessor to the Council is also present who, once the hearing has begun, opens proceedings by hearing the charges and ascertaining whether a notice of hearing has been received by the practitioner. He/she also advises those attending on points of law.

7. Notes are taken by a shorthand writer and a transcript is produced, which is a public document available on request and for a fee.

8. Evidence is given on oath.

9. Witnesses can be called by either side and can be asked questions by both sides and by the committee members.

10. The burden of proof is not as onerous as that of beyond reasonable doubt, but nonetheless a full investigation takes place and it is up to the person or organisation who has made the complaint to satisfy the committee that the complaint is well founded.

11. The complainant can attend if not giving evidence, and indeed members of the public can also attend hearings, but an appointment has to be made in advance because there is limited space for members of the public.

POSSIBLE OUTCOMES

(a) Case dismissed

13–33 This happens when there is insufficient evidence to substantiate the complaint, or the conduct is not judged to be infamous, all the evidence being heard.

(b) Judgment is postponed for a maximum of two years

13–34 This may seem a slightly unusual sanction, but the purpose of postponing judgment for up to two years is to enable the practitioner to take steps to improve his/her conduct. At the end of the period of postponement which has been stipulated by the committee, the case is referred back to the Committee for reassessment. At that point the Committee decides whether or not the practitioner has improved sufficiently to remain on the register, and whether no further action need be taken. This type of postponement will only take place if a practitioner has done something wrong, but the offence is not that serious.

(c) Removal of name from the Register

13–35 In cases which are proven, the Disciplinary Committee will order that the practitioner's name be struck from the register.

13–36 All parties are informed in writing of the decision of the Disciplinary Committee. Interestingly, professional bodies are also notified, as indeed are editors of professional journals.

In the past, meetings of the Disciplinary Committee have been relatively rare, but there has apparently been an increase in referrals to the Committee over the past year.

APPEALS

1. A respondent can appeal against a decision by the Disci- **13–37** plinary Committee within *28 days* of the decision.

2. The appeal must be made to the Privy Council.

3. At the time of writing, there has been no appeal from the decisions of the Disciplinary Committee.

CONCLUSION

The procedure seems effective in dealing with complaints about **13–38** registered members. However, at the moment the Council is unable to deal with the majority of complaints about competence, as infamous conduct is difficult to prove in this regard. It is also sometimes difficult to organise committees to deal with complaints when the Council and the Boards are independent of one another.

This is all going to change when a new Act comes into force **13–39** to update the existing system to sort out anomalies and/or problems which exist. The new Act is being drafted at the time of writing. Disciplinary powers will be conferred on the Council and will be extended to include clinical competence, and the number of available sanctions will be increased. The emphasis will remain on regulating the profession and maintaining high standards of professional practice and competence.

APPENDICES

LIST OF APPENDICES

APPENDIX A

ADDRESSES/CONTACT NUMBERS

Chapter 2

General Medical Council
178 Great Portland Street
London W1N 6JE

Tel: 0171 915 3603
Fax: 0171 915 3642

Chapter 3

Assistant Registrar
Professional Conduct
United Kingdom Central Council
    for Nursing, Midwifery and
    Health Visiting
23 Portland Place
London
W1N 4JT

Tel: 0171 637 7181
Fax:
General inquiries about
    complaints 0171 915 3603;
    0171 915 3642
Conduct procedures 0171 915
    3603; 0171 915 3642
Health procedures 0171 915
    3580; 0171 915 3696

Chapter 4

The British Dental Association
64 Wimpole Street
London
W1M 8Al

Tel: 0171 935 0875
Fax: 0171 487 5323

Registrar
General Dental Council
37 Wimpole Street
London
W1M 8DQ

Tel: 0171 887 3800

Chapter 5

The Royal Pharmaceutical
    Society
1 Lambeth High Street
London SE1 7JN

Tel: 0171 820 3399,
    Ext. 262/337
Fax: 0171 582 4279

Chapter 6

The General Osteopathic Council
Premier House
10 Greycoat Place
Victoria
London
SW1 15B

Chapter 7

The Chartered Society of
    Physiotherapy
14 Bedford Row
London WC1R 4ED

Tel: 0171 242 1941
Fax: 0171 831 4509

Chapter 8

The Registrar
General Optical Council
41 Harley Street
London W1N 2DJ

Tel: 0171 580 3898
Fax: 0171 436 3525

British College of Optometrists
42 Craven Street
London WC2N 5NG

Tel: 0171 839 6000
Fax: 0171 839 6800

The Association of British
Dispensing Opticians
6 Hurlingham Business Park
Sulivan Road
London SW6 3DU

Tel: 0171 736 0088
Fax: 0171 731 5531

Chapter 9

The British Chiropractic
Association
29 Whitley Street
Reading
Berkshire RG2 0EG

Tel: 0118 9757557
Fax: 0118 9757257

Chapter 10

The Royal College of Speech and
Language Therapists
7 Bath Place
Rivington Street
London EC2A 3DR

Tel: 0171 613 3855

Chapter 11

The Society of Homoeopaths
2 Artizan Road
Northampton NN1 4HU

Tel: 01604 621 400
Fax: 01604 622 622

Chapter 12

British Acupuncture Council
Park House
206/208 Latimer Road
London W10 6RE

Tel: 0181 964 0222
Fax: 0181 964 0333

Chapter 13

The Registrar
The Council for Professions
Supplementary to Medicine
Park House
184 Kennington Park Road
London SE11 4BU

Tel: 0171 582 0866
Fax: 0171 820 9684

The General Secretary
The Society of Chiropodists &
Podiatrists
53 Welbeck Street
London W1M 7HE

Tel: 0171 486 3381/4
Fax: 0171 935 6359

The Secretary
British Dietetic Association
7th Floor, Elizabeth House
22 Suffolk Street
Queensway Birmingham B1 1LS

Tel: 0121 643 5483
Fax: 0121 633 4399

The Secretary
College of Occupational
Therapists
6/8 Marshalsea Road
London SE1 1HL

Tel: 0171 357 6480
Fax: 0171 207 9612

The Executive Secretary
British Orthoptic Society
Tavistock House North
Tavistock Square
London WC1H 9HX

Tel: 0171 387 7992
Fax: 0171 383 2584

The General Secretary
Society of Radiographers
2 Carriage Row
183 Eversholt Street
London WC1R 4ED

Tel: 0171 391 4500
Fax: 0171 391 4504

The Administrator
Association of Professional Music
  Therapists
Chestnut Cottage
38 Pierce Lane
Fulbourn
Cambridge CB1 5DL

Tel: 01223 880377
Fax: 01233 881679

The British Association of
  Prosthetists & Orthotists
Sir James Clark Building
Abbey Mill Business Centre
Paisley
Renfrewshire PA1 1TJ

Tel: 0141 561 7217
Fax: 0141 561 7218

Other useful addresses

Health Service Commissioner for
  England
11th Floor
Millbank Tower
London SW1P 4QP

Tel: 0171 276 2035

Health Service Commissioner for
  Wales
4th Floor
Pearl Assurance House
Greyfriars Road
Cardiff
Wales CF1 3AG

Tel: 01222 394621

Health Information Service

Tel: 0800 665544

The Chief Executive
Institute of Biomedical Science
12 Coldbath Square
London EC1R 5HL

Tel: 0171 636 8192/5
Fax: 0171 436 4946

The Patients Association (PA)
P.O. Box 935
Harrow
Middlesex HA1 3YJ

Tel: 0181 423 8999
Fax: 0181 423 9119

Action for Victims of Medical
  Accidents (AVMA)
Bank Chambers
1 London Road
Forest Hill
London SE23 3TP

Tel/Fax: 0181 291 2841

Centre for Dispute Resolution
  (CEDR)
Princes House
95 Gresham Street
London EC2V 7NA

Tel: 0171 600 0500
Fax: 0171 600 0501

APPENDIX B

LIST OF ABBREVIATIONS

ADR	Alternative dispute resolution
AOR	Association of Reflexology
B.D.Sc.	Bachelor of Dental Science
B.Pharm.	Bachelor of Pharmacy
B.Sc.	Bachelor of Science—Clinical Communications (Speech and Language Therapists).
B.Sc.	Bachelor of Science
B.Sc.(Ost.)	Degree in Osteopathy
B.Sc.(Ost.)Med.	Member of the Royal Osteopathic Society
BCA	British Chiropractic Association
BDS	Bachelor of Dental Surgery
CEDR	Centre for Dispute Resolution
D.Ch.D.	Doctor of Dental Surgery
D.D.Sc.	Doctor of Dental Science
DDS	Doctor of Dental Surgery
FLCO	Fellow of the London College of Osteopathy
FLCOM	Fellow London College of Osteopathy Medicine
FRCGP	Fellow of the Royal College of General Practitioners
FRCP	Fellow of the Royal College of Physicians
FRCS	Fellow of the Royal College of Surgeons
FRPharmS	Fellow of the Royal Pharmaceutical Society of Great Britain
FSHom.	Fellow of the Society of Homoeopaths
GMC	General Medical Council
L.D.Sc.	Licentiate in Dental Science
LDS	Licentiate in Dental Surgery
M.D.Sc.	Master of Dental Science
M.Dent.Sc.	Master of Dental Surgery
MAOR	Member of the Association of Reflexology
MCSOT	Member of the Royal College of Speech and Language Therapy
MCSP	Member of the Chartered Society of Physiotherapists
MFPM RCP	Member Faculty Pharmaceutical Medicine Royal College Physicians
MPS/FPS	Member/Fellow (as appropriate) of the Pharmaceutical Society of Great Britain. *N.B.* This title fell into disuse when the Society received its Royal status, but some members still continue to use it.
MRO	Member of the Register of Osteopaths
MRPharmS	Member of the Royal Pharmaceutical Society of Great Britain
PCC	Professional Conduct Committee
PPC	Preliminary Proceedings Committee

211

RGN	Registered General Nurse
RSHom.	Registered in the Society of Homoeopaths
SRP	State Registered Physiotherapist
UKCC	United Kingdom Central Council for Nursing, Midwifery and Health Visiting

APPENDIX C

BIBLIOGRAPHY

The following booklets or sources of reference have been invaluable in the preparation of this book and serve as guidance to the procedures described:

1. The report of the Wilson Committee, "Being Heard" (1995).

2. GMC Publications:

   - "Facing a Complaint — the GMC's Conduct Procedures" (November 1997).
   - "When your Professional Performance is Questioned — the GMC's Performance Procedures" (November 1997).
   - "A problem with your Doctor — How the GMC deals with complaints" (November 1997).
   - "Helping Doctors Who are Ill — the GMC's Health Procedures" (November 1997).
   - "The Management of Doctors with Problems: Referral of Doctors to the GMC's Fitness to Practise Procedures" (July 1997).

3. UKCC — *Complaints about Professional Conduct* (August 1993).

4. General Dental Council — "Professional Conduct and Fitness to Practise, and Maintaining Standards of Guidance to Dentists on Personal and Professional Conduct" (May 1993).

5. The Chartered Society of Physiotherapy — Rules of Professional Conduct (November 1995).

6. The General Optical Council — booklet about the Council which includes details of the standard of professional competence.

7. British Chiropractic Association — Code of Disciplinary Procedure (1992).

8. The Royal College of Speech and Language Therapists — *Professional Standards* (republished 1996).

9. The Society of Homoeopaths:

   - Code of Ethics and Practice (July 1996).
   - Register of Homoeopaths — The Society of Homoeopaths, published annually.

10. British Acupuncture Council — Code of Professional Conduct (December 1995).

11. Council for Professions Supplementary to Medicine — "Who We Are and What We Do" (February 1997).

213

INDEX
(All references are to paragraph number)

219

Dismissal of complaints—*cont.*
  Professional Conduct
    Committee, byCSP, 7–63
  General Dental Council,
    4–37
  GMC, 2–157
  UKCC, 3–43
Doctors
  general practice, in
    generally, 2–01—2–07
    independent review,
      2–32—2–45
    local resolution, 2–20—2–31
    Ombudsman, 2–46—2–55
    relevant staff, 2–08—2–17
    time limits, 2–18—2–19
    local resolution, application
      for, 2–18—2–19
  mediation
    advantages, 2–238—2–247
    conclusion, 2–254—2–255
    disadvantages, 2–248—2–253
    generally, 2–211—2–214
    legal aid, 2–236—2–237
    procedure, 2–215—2–235
  NHS hospital, in
    generally, 2–01—2–07
    independent review,
      2–32—2–45
    local resolution, 2–20—2–31
    Ombudsman, 2–46—2–55
    relevant staff, 2–08—2–17
    time limits, 2–18—2–19
    local resolution, application
      for, 2–18—2–19
  private service, in
    generally, 2–56
    NHS patients in, 2–57—2–59

**Executive Committee (British
  Acupuncture Council),**
  12–07—12–08

Fine of member
  Disciplinary Committee, by
    BCA, 9–31, 9–45
  Disciplinary Officer, by
    BCA, 9–16

**General Council and Register of
  Osteopaths (GCRO)**
  and see General Osteopathic
    Council
  address, Appendix A
  generally, 6–01—6–10
General Dental Council
  address, Appendix A
  complaints procedure
    and see General Dental
      Council procedure
    conclusion, 4–60
    generally, 4–06—4–13
    procedure, 4–14—4–59
  composition, 4–01
  purpose, 4–02—4–05
**General Dental Council
  procedure**
  committee structure
    generally, 4–24
    Health Committee,
      4–41—4–59
    Preliminary Proceedings
      Committee, 4–25—4–32
    Professional Conduct
      Committee, 4–33—4–40
  complainants, 4–11—4–12
  conclusion, 4–60
  generally, 4–06—4–10
  Health Committee
    generally, 4–41
    powers, 4–52—4–59
    procedure, 4–42—4–51
  investigation by Council
    committee structure,
      4–24—4–59
    generally, 4–20—4–21
    procedure, 4–22
    time limits, 4–23
  local resolution, 4–14—4–17
  NHS complaints manager,
    4–18
  Notice of Inquiry, 4–61
  Ombudsman, 4–19
  Preliminary Proceedings
    Committee
    composition, 4–25
    powers, 4–27—4–32
    procedure, 4–26

230

Society of Homoeopaths procedure—*cont.*
preliminary investigation
generally, 11–36—11–37
procedure, 11–38—11–41
procedure
burden of proof, 11–29
complainants, 11–27
generally, 11–28
method, 11–30
structure, 11–31—11–83
purpose, 11–24—11–26
structure
formal procedure,
11–34—11–83
informal procedure,
11–31—11–33
Society of Osteopaths
address, Appendix A
Society of Radiographers
address, Appendix A
Speech therapists
complainants, 10–12
conclusion, 10–71
costs, 10–70
generally, 10–10
procedure
complainants, 10–12
costs, 10–70
structure, 10–13—10–69
time limits, 10–11
Professional Committee
appeals, 10–62—10–66
generally, 10–44—10–50
hearings, 10–51—10–54
powers, 10–55—10–69
Professional Director
conciliation, 10–30—10–33
formal procedure,
10–21—10–26
generally, 10–13—10–14
informal procedure,
10–15—10–20
investigation, 10–27—10–29
Screening Committee
generally, 10–34—10–35
powers, 10–42—10–43
procedure, 10–36—10–41
structure
generally, 10–13

Speech therapists—*cont.*
structure—*cont.*
Professional Committee,
10–43—10–69
Professional Director,
10–14—10–33
Screening Committee,
10–45—10–42
time limits, 10–11
Suspension of registration
and see Interim suspension
Disciplinary Committee, by
BCA, 9–46
General Optical Council,
8–30, 8–32
Health Committee, by
General Dental Council,
4–54
GMC, 2–123—2–124
Professional Conduct
Committee, by
College of Speech and
Language Therapists,
10–59
CSP, 7–67
General Dental Council,
4–39
GMC, 2–169—2–172

Time limits
College of Speech and
Language Therapists
procedure, 10–11
General Dental Council
procedure, 4–23
General Optical Council
procedure, 8–27
GMC procedure, 2–85
NHS procedure
independent review,
application for,
2–18—2–19
local resolution, application
for, 2–18—2–19
mediation, 2–216
Ombudsman, application to,
2–50—2–55

236